Energy Decentralization:
Sharing The Grid

By Austin Mardon, Pavel Zizler, Manahil Jawad, Noah Serethe, Monsur Moshood, Christina Nguyen, Faith Grace Robes, Hala Mahdi, Michael Phan, Freddie Montague, Alex Abraha, and Michelle Reinink

Edited by Catherine Mardon

Copyright © 2023 by Austin Mardon

All rights reserved. This book or any portion thereof may not be reproduced or used in any manner whatsoever without the express written permission of the publisher except for the use of brief quotations in a book review or scholarly journal.
First Printing: 2023

Cover Design by Samantha Lewin
Typeset by Samantha Lewin

Print ISBN: 978-1-77369-903-5
Ebook ISBN 978-1-312-79378-1

Golden Meteorite Press
103 11919 82 St NW
Edmonton, AB T5B 2W3
www.goldenmeteoritepress.com

IV

Contents

Introduction..Page 9

Chapter 1: Decentralized energy generation.............................Page 12

Chapter 2: Battery Storage..Page 22

Chapter 3: Managing Grid Stability and Smart Grids..............................Page 33

Chapter 4: Decentralized Energy Infrastructure..Page 43

Chapter 5: Residual Heat Distribution in Aircraft Systems.....................Page 56

Chapter 6: Combined Heat and Power.......................................Page 66

Chapter 7: Cities Around the World with 100% Sourced Renewable Energy ....Page 77

Chapter 8: Decentralized Wind Power.....................................Page 89

Chapter 9: Decentralized Solar Power..................................... Page 102

Chapter 10: Decentralized Hydro..Page 114

Chapter 11: The Forces Keeping Decentralized Energy Away................Page 124

Conclusion...Page 135

Introduction

The concepts of centralized and decentralized energy is often not spoken about in common discourse by individuals not directly affected by or working within the energy system. Many take for granted how energy is produced and how energy is delivered to their homes, cars, and businesses.
Traditionally, energy has been "Centralized", where one power plant is responsible for providing energy to a wide area of many homes. This centralized energy system must not only produce enough energy to supply the area, but also be able to reach the end users. This requires large power plants with a large amount of government infrastructure to be in place to ensure reliable and stable energy for the system. These centralized systems are often owned by the government, stifling competition and hindering the growth of a small business market. The large power requirement has restricted governments to rely on tried and tested energy sources, such as fossil fuels to reliable produce massive amounts of energy. However, fossil fuels have a tendency to produce harmful gasses and by products which has resulted in almost irreparable environmental damage.

In contrast to "Centralized" energy, "Decentralized" energy is proposed. This requires smaller power production units, catered to small areas, allowing the producers and users to better communicate, leading to smaller infrastructure and more flexibility in terms of production methods and distribution solutions. Chapter 1 deals with decentralized energy generation, where energy is produced closer to the areas which require it. This solution is explored for its rapid response to changing factors, ability to have a flexible energy production source, such as renewables, and lead to lower efficiency drops.

Chapter 2 tackles a common problem of decentralized and renewable energy sources, reliability. This chapter explores battery systems for storage of energy produced by renewables. Battery solutions are explored in detail, and the availability of different types of batteries are discussed.

Chapter 3 describes how smart grids may be used by decentralized energy systems to better achieve efficiency and smoothness of available energy. The smart grid uses automation to better organize distribution of the energy produced.

Chapter 4 looks into decentralized energy infrastructure and the requirements needed to implement a decentralized energy system.

Chapter 5 completes a detailed review of residual energy distribution, specifically on airplanes. A significant amount of heat is lost in airplane engines which running and is not recovered and used again. This chapter looks into the problems of excessive heat production in airplanes and the potential solutions to this problem.

Chapter 6 looks at residual energy distribution more generally, and looks into the system of combined heat and power system, where excess heat energy is not wasted, but used for other productive purposes.

Chapter 7 does a detailed dive into how cities, which has already transitioned to renewable energy, have achieved this feat. The chapter looks into the solutions of these cities and why renewable energy was so readily available to these geographic regions. The chapter also explores some of the political and ideological motivations for the transition to renewable energy.

Chapter 8 looks into how wind power may be used to decentralized energy systems, and how this form of renewable energy is a suitable choice for the decentralization of energy systems.

Chapter 9, like chapter 8 looks into renewable energy production and how it is suitable for decentralization. However, this chapter focuses on solar energy production and how individuals and small groups may be able to use solar energy to decentralize the energy production in given regions.

Chapter 10 looks into hyrdo-power decentralization. This chapter also looks at smart contracts, through an open-source project called hydro. Both of these technologies are viewed in light of decentralization of energy infrastructure.

Chapter 11 explores the hesitancy of adopting renewable energy, and decentralization of energy production. This chapter explores why decentralization has been achieved with the technology available and the hesitancy of individuals, groups, corporations and governments to decentralization.

Chapter 1
Decentralized Energy Generation

Pavel Zizler

Introduction

Decentralization is the act of a large government or an organizational body to spread out its power to lower subdivisions of organization or government bodies (Brown, 2009). As this may lower the control and regulation of major responsibilities, the ability to delegate powers and responsibilities to lower groups is the main basis to decentralization. This method allows the organizations to make specific, and effective decisions that can benefit not only the individual localities, but also the entire division of government as a whole. In simpler terms decentralization is based on shifting from a larger organization to many smaller divisions. This method is essentially the opposite of monopolization, which is the process of controlling a larger body without the possibility of sharing.

The meaning of decentralizing energy is the action of spreading energy production to places closer to where energy is used. (Imbault et al. 2017). This concept is often confused with decentralization as a whole, a slightly different term. However, the concepts are similar and will be discussed in further detail below.

Developing countries around the world often use decentralization as an important method in aiding the development of facilities, government institutions, and overall urban/rural infrastructure improvements (Rondinelli et al. 1983). This method has often led to increased levels of development activities, programs, and government bodies. However, the challenges of implementation of decentralization has halted many countries from being able to take the next step in development. One of the main challenges faced by developing countries in decentralizing their energy was the inability to generate enough political and bureaucratic support to allocate enough funds. Another important aspect which normally could not be met was generating overall population support. This causes the idea of decentralization to be more theoretical, rather than a practical manner to power the development of countries. Many political leaders regard centralization as the desireable structure because of the ability to easily regulate and control the development, while not investing funds to generate the spread of power to smaller subdivisions. With developing countries failing to fully incorporate decentralization, this method in energy generation must overcome obstacles found in developing countries to fully utilize the power of this system method.

In order for decentralization to be optimally utilized certain conditions must be met to keep organization and structure. First, in order to fully transition into decentralization, a secure existence must be met for each subdivision that is given power (Kalin, 1999). Without a secure existence, the subdivisions would easily be overthrown by the larger organizations in the event where the specific locality did not achieve the requirements set out by the larger organization. Second, resources and autonomy are an important characteristic in a decentralized organization. The ability of a subdivision to be autonomous allows for the decisions and responsibilities to be fully specialized to the specific locality. For example, a government decentralizing into smaller local domains the ability of localities to be fully autonomous allows them to make specific investments on the specific regions. This is in contrast to a larger body making decisions for the entire country. If the smaller divisions are not fully in control of their localities decentralization will not work out. Resources are also a critical characteristic in decentralization, because it allows the subdivisions to have the tools to behave autonomously and to make the correct decisions to benefit the locality. Lastly, political-will is the most important characteristic that is necessary to build a prosperous decentralized organization. In developing countries decentralization failed to produce an excelling development plan because of the inability of political powers and governments to fully commit to a decentralization of development in countries. Because of this the art of political-will is crucial as it allows the subdivisions to be fully autonomous, have a healthy influx of resources, and inherit a secure existence.

Energy Generation and Climate Change

Climate change, the long term increase or decrease of temperature in global climates, directly impacts the future of energy generation and the act of decentralization. Changing climate conditions can affect energy supply and demand, energy transportation, and infrastructure use in the global energy scale (Schaeffer et al. 2012). In the initial stages of energy generation, resources are the prized possession because the amount of resources also determines the amount of energy available for use. With respect to fossil fuels many scientists argue the consequences of using these resources on the environment. On the other hand, renewable energy resouces are overall better for the climate and environment, renewable sources include energy production such as wind power generation and hydro powered generation. Because of this a change in global climate may also affect these sources of energy, which is an important aspect scientists must consider when discussing the impacts of cutting fossil fuel use, and relying more on renewable energy.

Hydro power generation is dependent on the climate to provide availability of water resources, and to power the energy that ultimately comes from the runoff of water (Schaeffer et al. 2012). Hydro power requires excess water as a source of an energy resource, commonly in the form of runoffs. Because of this, the hydrological cycle is crucial to this hydro-energy production as it is directly impacted by the changes in climate. Specifically, in regions where the melting of snow delivers the source of runoffs, the warming or cooling climate can enormously affect the output of energy generation whether it is increased or decreased. These power plants rely on the cycle of snowmelt in these regions and even slight changes in this cycle can pose detrimental conflicts to the ultimate source of energy. Scientists must examine the hydrological cycle and the effects of climate change to fully assess the ability of hydro power generation and to maximize its potential.

Similarily, the second ranked renewable energy source in the world, wind power, is also affected by changes in climate (Pryor and Barthelmie, 2010). This use of energy is only projected to increase in the efforts of promoting renewable energy sources. The reliability and availability of this source of energy is greatly dependent on climate, specifically atmospheric motion. WIth a disruption in this atmospheric motion, the overall wind powered system will become disorganized, and potentially decrease the energy output provided by the system. Despite the challenges, wind energy is still a leading contributor to renewable energy.

Intro to Nuclear Fusion

Recognized by many scientists as the "holy grail" of renewable energy, nuclear fusion can be an interesting development within the pursuit of renewable energy sources for widespread energy consumption. Nuclear fusion has been in development since 1920 and continues on today. The aim is to be an excellent source of energy, while also being renewable and clean to the environment. Nuclear fusion, also known as Nuclear Combustion is an occurrence where the nuclei of certain isotopes collide and merge into one, releasing energy (Post, 1976). Interestingly, this source of energy was later identified as the one used by many stars in the universe, including the sun. However, because we cannot reproduce the sun's method of energy generation, scientists developed the method of using a heavy hydrogen isotope, also known as deuterium to use within the process. This was done because regular hydrogen cannot be used unless within the parameters of a chemical process unavailable to humans within the earth's atmosphere at the moment. Deuterium has the ability to release 10 million times more energy per gram vs fossil fuels, suggesting just the power of this method of energy generation. It is important to note that this statistic is measured per gram, which can be misleading, but the overall concept is still the same. Post (1976) deduced that the supply of deuterium in the oceans can fund the energy needed for the world for 100 billion years, which doesn't even come close to the expected lifetime of our universe. Because of this, if nuclear fusion develops practically, there will not be a more sustainable form of energy that can power the entire world. However, it is important to note that the separation of this heavy isotope of hydrogen requires energy to separate it from water, thus indicating that some energy investment must be made. In regards to the bigger picture, the ability of scientists to discover this phenomenon was a great indication of the importance of decentralizing energy generation.

The benefits of nuclear power as a substitute for other energy generation methods all relate strongly to producing a more clean, renewable, energy source. With a big portion of European countries aiming to move towards a carbon free economy by 2050, the ability to find a source of energy that is carbon neutral, is absolutely essential (Čabelkova et al. 2021). Conveniently, Colin (2022) highlights that the number one benefit to using nuclear power as an energy source is the ability to generate energy without the use of carbon. This directly outlines Europe's goals for energy generation should be a main focus point of research to be able to make this energy source practical. Another crucial benefit to nuclear powered energy is the elimination of having pollution as a heavy byproduct. This byproduct is often a driving cause of greenhouse gas emissions, which ultimately drives climate change. A disadvantage to this phenomenon is mainly the high cost investment prices.

Decentralization of Energy

A proposed decentralization of energy would consist of the transfer of power to lower authorities, to ultimately run energy generation as a collective unit. Because of this, it will allow the diversification of energy use and generation. This led to new inventions and propositions, such as nuclear fusion, while also leading to the ultimate solution of a prime renewable energy source. This prime renewable energy source would be fully sustainable while having limited harm to the environment, which ultimately decreases the carbon footprint for any individual running power using this energy generation. Without the decentralization of energy this would not be possible, or much more difficult to control, fund, and allocate sufficient resources. Leal-Arcas (2019) discusses the progress of energy decentralization in the European Union (EU), and strong implementation of these policies will lead to increased prosperity in the overall fight for a prime renewable energy resource. While the energy market in Europe seems to be still in a monopolized form, which causes complications to the goal of sustainable development. This sustainability is a common goal for all EU countries. Unreliable oil producers, and unsettled geopolitical conflict will not only limit the progress to sustainable energy, it will halt the process completely. Because of this, the EU is actively trying to mitigate this issue by decentralizing energy sources and generation. Leal-Arcas (2019) describes the EU's goals to shift from large energy stations, into smaller, local energy grids that can lead to the diversification of energy, which will ultimately allow for the flexibility of energy use, which will benefit the factors that contribute to the shift to decentralized energy. Addressing climate change can be done by reducing greenhouse gas emissions, increasing energy use/efficiency. Additional security of energy can be improved by limiting imports. and prioritizing renewable energy sources. The European Union performing a colossal transformation in the priorities of energy generation and the models of decentralized energy, involves a complete diversification that cannot be done overnight. In regards to this, the EU has set out many climate and renewable energy plans that will accelerate this transition, and ultimately display prosperous results.

Guo et al. (2010) discusses a proposed idea of the Smart Grid, which are specific marketplaces that are consumer driven, to provide distributed generation of energy. The main characteristic of this method of planning is involving the direct relationship between consumers and markets. This is the root driving force of decentralized energy, and is the primary factor to this increase of prosperity. Connecting consumers with the energy market will involve a handful of benefits, most importantly, the ability to use localized subdivisions of the energy market. This is opposed to having large units of power stations. Without the direct connection between consumers and the market, the act of decentralization would not be possible. In addition, Guo et al. (2013) describes the importance of adaptive market styles, and the ability to resist fluctuating changes in the overall energy market. Smart Grid eliminates this threat, by providing locality within the energy market. Because of this, the diversification of the energy supply and generation will resist common changes and problems, due to the localized and distributed sources. In a centralized method of energy, this would not be possible because any changes that may be found, would directly impact the entire unit. This would force the entire unit to make changes to counteract these issues, rather than diversified localities using their powers to resist these issues. An analogy to this would be diversifying investments in the stock market, which overall decreases risk and volatility, while improving potential returns. Diversifying your stock investments and decentralizing energy are related, and have the same ideas.

Why is Decentralization Important?
Number 1: Any conflicts and tension that can be caused by a superior power can be a cause for major troubles in a company, country, or any possible

workplace. This is because in a centralized method, there can be various conflicts which can cause division in opinions and values. In a decentralized system, this is limited because of the abilities of smaller divisions to do what is best for them and solve minor tensions at their discretion. In addition, any potential conflicts and tension are overall less likely to happen in these divisions because of the more controlled environments in a smaller group. For example, a large company when making major decisions for the future or present, will have increased division and tension. On the other hand, dividing the power of that larger company in different sectors, will result in less tension. This is because the overall stress is decreased in implementing decisions on a smaller scale. In terms of decentralizing and diversifying energy, determining which energy source is most efficient while being renewable and green can cause tension in the entire energy sector. Because of this countries and companies may transition to more renewable energy sources through decentralization of energy.

Number 2: Decentralization promotes expansion. Decentralization promotes expansion of new ideas, topics, and methods. This is mainly because in a diversified corporation or government, there is an increased motive to brainstorm new ideas. In the topic of energy decentralization, the ability to find new ways to produce clean, green energy, would be more lucrative within a diversified system. Decentralizing energy sources and generation can prove to provide efficiency, while also finding renewable and green energy. In a centralized system, the overall governance and brainstorming is very limited, and rigid. Using university as an analogy, a classic university does not have a single department for students. These different divisions are created to have a diversified and specific topic for each department. This may include arts, science, engineering, business, etc. In this case, all universities can be seen as at least partially decentralized due to the separate systems and division of departments and faculties. Through these faculties, there have been expansions in many universities of different degrees and courses. This accelerated expansion was only evident because of the breakdown of power in these specific faculties and departments. Although a very general example, this university system highlights the basis of decentralization in a very simple, and effective way.

Number 3: Specificity of needs. In a decentralized system, the ability to have specific divisions of power is very lucrative and beneficial. Centralization, where there is one large system of power, has a common disadvantage of being rigid and general. In regards to energy, a proposed division can be created specifically for green energy while another division can focus on renewable energy, and there can even be another division that focuses on efficient energy. The list can go on and on, with countless branches of different sectors for the overall energy system. This can prove to have energy sources that are great for the overall environment, while also proving to be efficient. WIthout this method in play, the energy generation methods will be limited, with new, lucrative ideas being hard to come by.

Negatives to Decentralized Energy

Number 1: The cost of a decentralized energy system can be a detrimental factor to the system itself. The cost to organize all these different subdivisions, fund resources, and keep overall structure may pose many negatives to the system. Because of this, many countries, companies have shifted to a more centralized method. In the energy world, having many diversified methods of energy can prove to be costly, and energy inefficient. Many energy sectors often choose the route of centralizing their energy source to value quality over quantity. Because of this, there can be more quality in the sources of energy in terms of efficiency.

Number 2: Controlling different types of energy sources can prove to provide stress and inefficiency to the overall energy world. The option of distributing energy across where it will be used, rather than large power plants, can suggest a loss of regulation among these localities. In a centralized energy system, the large divisions of power plants can be heavily and easily controlled and regulated. This is the case for decentralizing and diversifying anything, whether it is stocks, or a business, there is a loss of control over all the divisions. However, many studies suggest that although these negative effects can suggest that decentralization in energy can be a tension riddled process, they are just simple bumps to the overall journey of decentralizing energy sectors.

Conclusion

Decentralizing energy, like decentralizing other aspects of business, can prove to be extremely beneficial for increased efficiency and overall prosperity. In regards to decentralization of energy, diversifying and spreading out energy sectors in closer proximity to where energy is used can prove to provide a loss of stress/tension on energy, provide more expansional ideas, and allow for a clear specificity of needs among the entire sector. These benefits can also be expanded to an increased use of renewable energy, and the overall increase of eco-efficient products. Bearing the negatives in mind, the decentralization of energy can prove to be beneficial to the environment. In addition to this, it can lower the carbon footprint, and contribute to an overall greener economy. Decentralization is the future.

References

Brown T. "Health Services Restructuring". International Encyclopedia of Human Geography 0:(2009): 51-57

Čábelková, Inna, et al. "The social acceptance of nuclear fusion for decision making towards carbon free circular economy: Evidence from Czech Republic." Technological Forecasting and Social Change 163 (2021): 120477.

Colin, R. "Pros and Cons of Nuclear Fusion and their Benefits and Drawbacks." (2022).

Guo, Yuanxiong, et al. "Decentralized coordination of energy utilization for residential households in the smart grid." IEEE transactions on smart grid 4.3 (2013): 1341-1350.

Imbault, Fabien, et al. "The green blockchain: Managing decentralized energy production and consumption." 2017 IEEE International Conference on Environment and Electrical Engineering and 2017 IEEE Industrial and Commercial Power Systems Europe (EEEIC/I&CPS Europe). IEEE, 2017.

Kälin, Walter. "Decentralization–Why and how." Decentralization and development. Bern: Swiss Agency for Development and Cooperation

Publications on Development(1999).

Schaeffer, Roberto, et al. "Energy sector vulnerability to climate change: A review." Energy 38.1 (2012): 1-12.

Leal-Arcas, Rafael, Juan Alemany Rios, and Nelson Akondo. "Energy decentralization in the European Union." Georgetown Environmental Law Review 32 (2019).

Altmann, M., Brenninkmeijer, A., Lanoix, J. C., Ellison, D., Crisan, A., Hugyecz, A., ... & Hänninen, S. "Decentralized energy systems" (2010).

Post, Richard F. "Nuclear fusion." Annual Review of Energy 1.1 (1976): 213-255.

Pryor, Sara C., and R. J. Barthelmie. "Climate change impacts on wind energy: A review." Renewable and sustainable energy reviews 14.1 (2010): 430-437.

Rondinelli, Dennis A., John R. Nellis, and G. Shabbir Cheema. "Decentralization in developing countries." World Bank staff working paper 581 (1983): 13-28.

Chapter 2
Battery Storage

Manahil Jawad

Energy storage is vital to decarbonizing the power system and reducing emissions of greenhouse gasses. It is also necessary to build affordable, reliable and resilient electricity grids which can deal with the changeable nature of renewable energy sources such as solar and wind (Faunce et al.). There are various methods to store energy, from rechargeable batteries in electric vehicles to extensive facilities that compress air and release it to drive turbines that generate electricity. Regardless of the method, it is evident that storage is a very flexible and valuable source of electricity (Raugei et al.). It acts as a form of supply and demand, drawing electricity from the grid when demand is low and releasing energy into the grid when demand is high. In particular, the storage helps support the wide-scale combination of renewable resources, such as wind and solar, because it can cover reduced energy output caused by sudden weather changes.

The electricity industry faces new challenges not seen in 100 years because consumers are becoming more active, and power producers demand reliable, clean, affordable power. Therefore, the transforming grid needs novel technological solutions to unlock new business models and revenue schemes (Raugei et al.). The future of the energy sector has always been linked with the reality that humanity will learn to build up energy successfully and use it when needed. The future is bright as it comes more confidently and with different efficiency (Faunce et al.). There are different types of energy storage solutions available today. The different types of energy storage include battery, thermal, flywheels, compressed air, pumped hydro storage and hydrogen storage. However, lithium-ion batteries are the technology of choice due to their cost-effectiveness and high efficiency (Faunce et al.).

What is battery storage?

Battery storage technologies are essential to speed up the replacement of fossil fuels with renewable energy. Regardless of their nature, battery storage systems will play an increasingly crucial role between green energy supplies and responding to electricity demands (Raugei et al.). Battery storage, or battery energy storage systems (BESS), allow energy from renewables such as solar and wind to be stored and released when customers require the power most. BESS are advanced technology solutions that provide multiple ways to store energy. These rechargeable batteries can store energy from diverse sources and can be discharged when needed. BESS consists of one or more batteries, provides grid stability and backup power and can be used to balance the electric grid (Raugei et al.). The energy stored in the BESS can also be saved for later use. Lithium-ion batteries (used in mobile phones and electric cars) are the dominant storage technology for large-scale plants to help electricity grids ensure a reliable supply of renewable energy. These batteries preserve energy until it is required, making them a flexible and reliable source of electrical energy (Yuan et al.).

Benefits of Battery Storage

There are various benefits of battery storage. The benefits of battery energy storage include higher energy efficiency, savings, greater flexibility and scalability, lower cost and sustainability by lowering consumption. An energy supply can experience fluctuations due to weather, blackouts, or geopolitical reasons; batteries are vital for utilities, businesses and homes to achieve a continual power flow. Therefore, energy storage systems are no longer an afterthought or an add-on (Kim et al.).

Backup Power

Backup power requires batteries that can keep some necessities running in situations involving outage like grid failures and power shutoffs. You can avoid darkness by tapping into your private energy reservoir using battery storage systems (Kim et al.).

Green Energy
Batteries provide an opportunity to store clean and green energy from wind and solar so that you can access it when needed (Kim et al.).

One step closer to grid independence
The solar panels produce abundant electricity while the sun shines. Excess energy produced by the panels is collected and saved during the day through battery storage, which can be used when needed (Kim et al.).

Lower energy bills
Generally, the electricity rates are highest after work and in the evening, when your solar panels produce less power. Using your stored energy during expensive peak rate periods helps neutralize time-of-use rates and significantly decrease energy costs and bills (Faunce et al.).

Decrease carbon footprint
Pairing solar panel systems with intelligent energy storage transforms the place into a sustainable, eco-friendly residence. Most or all of the power is generated with zero emissions, thus reducing reliance on the fossil fuel-powered utility grid (Kim et al.).

Battery storage adds efficiency
Battery storage is the second component of a sustainable solar energy system. A battery storage system can store excess solar power generated by the panels (Joseph and Shahidehpour). At night you can draw on this power, thus decreasing the amount of power drawn from the grid. Backup power is also provided by the storage system that allows you to keep your home up and to run during a planned or unplanned power outage.

Why is battery storage important?
Battery storage technology has played a key part in ensuring that homes and businesses can be powered by green energy, even when the sun is not shining, or the wind has stopped blowing (Joseph and Shahidehpour). For example, the UK has the largest installed offshore wind capacity worldwide. Still, with the capability to detain this energy and with purposeful deployment, the value

of this clean energy can be increased (by increasing production and reducing costs). As per the estimates by the UK government, technologies like battery storage systems (BESS), which support the integration of more low-carbon power, heat and transport technologies, could save the UK energy system up to £40 billion ($48 billion) by 2050, eventually reducing energy bills of the people (Joseph and Shahidehpour). According to Ken-Ichi Hino, Director of Energy at National Grid Renewables in the US, "Storage enables further renewable generation, both from an operational and reliability viewpoint. It's also a key piece of our utility customers' ongoing evolution and transition to renewables. We see an important opportunity for pairing energy storage with our solar projects moving forward." Therefore, BESS is the future.

How does a battery storage system work?

A battery storage system can be charged by electricity generated from wind and solar power, renewable energies. BESS are significantly more advanced than the batteries we keep in our kitchen drawer or insert in our children's toys (Joseph and Shahidehpour). Intelligent battery softwares uses algorithms to coordinate energy production. In contrast, computerized control systems are utilized to decide when to release or keep the energy to provide to the reserves when required. The battery storage system is a closed loop. During peak demand, energy is released from the battery storage system, keeping the costs down and the energy remains in the system when it is not needed (Joseph and Shahidehpour). The closed-loop system makes the BESS a low-cost option and provides stable energy.

Renewable energy storage systems-Technologies

Renewable energy storage needs low-cost technologies that have long lives, charge and discharge thousands of times, are safe, and can store sufficient energy cost-effectively to match demand. In the 1970s, British scientists developed Lithium-ion batteries. In 1991, lithium-ion batteries were first used commercially by Sony for the company's handheld video recorder (Kim et al.). Although they are still the most economically viable energy storage solution, several other technologies for battery storage are currently being developed, as discussed below. According to Prescott Hartshorne, Director of Distributed Energy and Renewables for National Grid Ventures "the next decade will be big for energy storage in general and batteries in particular. It will be a significant proving time for batteries and other technologies".

Compressed air energy storage

Compressed air energy storage is generally located in oversized chambers, surplus power is used to compress and store air. When energy is required, the compressed air is released and passes through an air turbine to generate electricity (Kim et al.).

Mechanical gravity energy storage

One example of this system is when energy is used to lift concrete blocks up a tower. When the energy is required, the concrete blocks are lowered back down, generating electricity using the pull of gravity (Kim et al.).

Flow batteries

Flow batteries are batteries that contain rechargeable fuel cells. The batteries consist of two chemical components dissolved in liquids separated by a membrane contained within the system to provide chemical energy (Kim et al.).

Challenges & Opportunities of Energy Storage

By storing the energy, we are transforming how we generate and use electricity by ensuring that surplus energy is stored until needed. Energy storage improves energy security by providing backup power to: homes, businesses, and communities, and supports the wide-scale integrations of renewables (Faunce et al.). In addition, energy storage helps maintain the reliability of the grid. It enables us to draw electricity when demand is low and release stored energy when it is high. There are three powerful trends that have driven this change to energy generation and consumption. First is the arrival of increasingly affordable distributed power technologies (Faunce et al.). Secondly, is the decarbonization of the world's electricity network through introducing more renewable energy sources, and thirdly the emergence of digital technologies (Faunce et al.).

Decarbonization

The rapid deployment of low-carbon technologies like wind and solar makes it increasingly difficult to anticipate variable generation, creating challenges around grid stability, congestion and market volatility (Faunce et al.).

Digitization

On dynamic and nominal prices, connected devices and smart sensors create fast decision-making, while intelligent control systems and internet-enabled software optimize the power plants and the grid (Faunce et al.).

Decentralization

With the growing penetration of distributed energy resources along with renewables and storage, more armatures have been created, increasing distribution grid complexity and decentralization (Faunce et al.).

Solar Energy Storage

When combined with solar energy, battery energy storage is particularly effective and more successful. Solar energy storage not only mitigates the irregular nature of renewable power but also guarantees a stable supply of electricity. The batteries in a solar energy storage system are charged during the day, and when the sun is not shining, batteries release power. Generally, a built-in inverter changes the DC current generated by solar panels into the AC current. The change to AC current powers appliances and equipment for a business or home solar energy system. Solar battery storage works with an energy management system (EMS) that manages both charge and discharge cycles based on real-time requirements and availability.

Applications of Battery Storage

Main battery storage differs depending on the type of storage, that is, whether the storage is being undertaken and used for a home or for a business. It can be used in many ways beyond the simple emergency backup in the event of an energy shortage or blackout. There are several applications for commercial and industrial users, including peak shaving, load shifting, flexibility, microgrids and integration with renewable energy sources.

Peak shaving

Peak shaving is the ability to manage energy demand to evade an abrupt short-term spike in consumption (Yuan et al.). Battery storage systems allow you to utilize energy storage by switching equipment on and off to accomplish peak shaving.

Load shifting

Load shifting allows businesses to shift their energy consumption from one time period to another by tapping the battery when energy costs more, allowing businesses to choose the more cost-effective option (Yuan et al.).

Flexibility

Customers can reduce their site's grid demand without changing their electricity consumption at crucial times. Therefore, energy storage makes it much easier to contribute to a demand Response program and save on energy costs, providing more flexibility for customers (Yuan et al.).

Microgrid

This application relies on batteries as a key element. Microgrids need energy storage to disconnect from the main electricity grid when required; therefore, batteries are crucial to the function of microgrids (Yuan et al.).

Integration with renewable energy sources

When there is no integration with renewable energy sources, power from renewables, batteries guarantee a smooth and continuous electricity flow (Yuan et al.).

Applications for Residential users: There are also various applications through which residential users benefit from battery storage as appended below:

Self-consumption

Residential users can produce solar energy during daylight hours and then run their appliances at home at night (Yuan et al.). In the event of an emergency or a blackout, the stored energy can be utilized as an emergency backup (Yuan et al.). Another application for residential users is going off the grid. Storing energy can also allow going off the grid or detaching completely from an electrical or energy utility.

Different Types of Meter Systems- Battery Energy Storage

There are two types of battery energy storage systems (BESS). These are front-of-the-meter (FTM) or behind-the-meter (BTM). BTM systems are typically smaller than FTM systems and installed on the user's premises. The main function of the BTM is to improve the stability of its owners' energy supply and cut costs (Zhao et al.). The batteries can also supply energy back into the grid and become an added revenue stream if the local regulatory framework allows it. In contrast, the larger FTM systems are directly connected to the power grid and generally belong to a utility, which helps solve network congestion issues or can serve as an alternative to building new power lines (Zhao et al.).

Battery Energy Storage lasting & its Second Life

Normally, most battery storage energy systems (BESS) last 5-15 years. BESS are tools that enable sustainability as part of the ecosystem of solutions for the energy transition. At the same time, they must be fully sustainable. The recycling of the materials and reuse of batteries at the end of their life are all-around sustainability goals and an effective application of Circular Economy principles. Giving them a second life through recovering an increasing quantity of materials from batteries leads to environmental benefits in the extraction and disposal stages. Reuse of batteries also delivers economic benefits.

Integration with Distributed Generation System & Supporting Electric Grid
Battery storage systems like Enel X are equipped with DER OS optimization software. This software is designed to work with all types of distributed energy resources and can easily be integrated into existing systems, like solar photovoltaic systems (Tagliafierro). Batteries store power generated by facilities when the sun is shining, then the stored power is dispatched to the grid to supplement dips in operation. Especially when clouds roll in and temporarily reduce the sunlight reaching the panels of a solar plant (Tagliafierro). During peak customer electricity demand, such as evening hours and summer afternoons when the sun is going down, but air conditioning needs remain high, the stored power can also be dispatched. An effective solution for all energy

scenarios can be created regardless of whether a business already has battery storage systems up and running in its facilities or needs to integrate them with a battery storage system (Tagliafierro).

Battery Storage System Initiatives & Projects- USA & Canada

In the USA and Canada, many projects and initiatives have been undertaken by the public and private sectors for battery storage systems given their utility, significance and need. In the USA, NextEra is an energy storage leader that has more energy storage capacity than any other company in the USA. It has more than 180 MW of battery energy storage systems in operation to ensure that Americans have the needed energy (Jordaan et al.). The company that continues to lead the industry with novelty includes Babcock Ranch Solar Energy Centre, the largest combined solar plus storage facility in the USA. This project incorporates a 10 MW battery storage project into the operations of a 74.4MW solar power plant. Second is in Arizona, a 20MW central solar energy center which is the first project to pair solar energy with a site 10 MW battery storage system (Jordaan et al.). This facility stores excess energy in a lithium-ion battery storage system besides generating sufficient solar energy to power 5000 homes. Another is Florida power & light Wynwood energy storage facility featuring a 10MW/40MWh battery system, which dispatches enough energy to either power 7000 homes or to charge 5mn mobile phones for 4 hours (Jordaan et al.).

Likewise, in Canada, many projects and initiatives have been undertaken. This is due to the fact that battery storage pilot programs, such as that in Nova Scotia, have already successfully tested battery storage at a community level for customers.. Such pilot programs and testing phases have helped understand how batteries can allow storage and use of renewable energy more effectively and efficiently. In addition, it demonstrates the reliability of this backup energy technology (Jordaan et al.). One such project is the intelligent feeder project making renewable energy more efficient and customer power supply more secure. It is undertaken in Elmsdale, Nova Scotia.Nova Scotia Power works with customers and industry leaders to examine how battery technology and microgrids can help us better serve their customers (Jordaan et al.). This pilot project is helping in understanding how batteries can help use renewable energy more efficiently while providing backup power to customers during power outages.

Partners of this pilot project are Opus One Solutions which has provided the software that monitors electrical system activity and optimizes battery usage, and the other is Sustainable Development Technology Canada. At the local substation, residential Tesla batteries have also been installed at ten homes in Elmsdale (5 kW/13.5 kWh) and a one grid-sized Tesla Powerpack (1.225 MW/2.45 MWh).

Conclusion

Battery storage enables us to store power generated at nearby wind farms and supply that electricity to the grid to match customer demand. Though Nova Scotia is one of the best places in Canada to harness the power of wind, because both wind and solar power sourses are intermittent, they need reliable backup energy (Joseph and Shahidehpour). That is where battery storage comes in, for which efforts and works are underway to achieve 60% of electricity from clean energy sources like wind and solar. To modernize the power grid, the key is an investment in new technology, and the first choice is battery storage.

References

"Battery Storage: Your Questions Answered." National Grid Group, https://www.nationalgrid.com/stories/energy-explained/what-is-battery-storage

"Battery Storage: Store Energy to Use Later in Your Home." Default, https://www.nspower.ca/your-home/energy-products/battery-storage.

"Ontario's Electricity Grid." Energy Storage, https://www.ieso.ca/en/Learn/Ontario-Electricity-Grid/Energy-Storage.

"What Is Battery Energy Storage System and How It Works." Enel X, https://corporate.enelx.com/en/question-and-answers/what-is-battery-energy-storage.

"Battery Energy Storage Solutions: Bess: Storage Solutions: Siemens Energy Global." Siemens, https://www.siemens-energy.com/global/en/offerings

"Benefits of Battery Storage." Panasonic Canada | Technologies That Move Us, https://na.panasonic.com/ca/benefits-battery-storage.

Raugei, Marco, et al. "What Are the Energy and Environmental Impacts of Adding Battery Storage to Photovoltaics? A Generalized Life Cycle Assessment." Energy Technology, vol. 8, no. 11, 2020, p. 1901146., https://doi.org/10.1002/ente.201901146.

Jordaan, Sarah M., et al. "Innovation in Intermittent Electricity and Stationary Energy Storage in the United States and Canada: A Review." Renewable and Sustainable Energy Reviews, vol. 158, 2022, p. 112149., https://doi.org/10.1016/j.rser.2022.112149.

Zhao, Haoran, et al. "Comprehensive Performance Assessment on Various Battery Energy Storage Systems." Energies, vol. 11, no. 10, 2018, p. 2841., https://doi.org/10.3390/en11102841.

Tagliafierro, Nicola. "The Circular Economy at Enel X." Symphonya. Emerging Issues in Management, no. 1, 2020, p. 101., https://doi.org/10.4468/2020.1.08tagliafierro.

Joseph, A., and M. Shahidehpour. "Battery Storage Systems in Electric Power Systems." 2006 IEEE Power Engineering Society General Meeting, 2006, https://doi.org/10.1109/pes.2006.1709235.

Yuan, Yue, et al. "Applications of Battery Energy Storage System for Wind Power Dispatchability Purpose." Electric Power Systems Research, vol. 93, 2012, pp. 54–60., https://doi.org/10.1016/j.epsr.2012.07.008.

Faunce, Thomas A., et al. "On-Grid Batteries for Large-Scale Energy Storage: Challenges and Opportunities for Policy and Technology." MRS Energy & Sustainability, vol. 5, no. 1, 2018, https://doi.org/10.1557/mre.2018.11.

Kim, Taehoon, et al. "Lithium-Ion Batteries: Outlook on Present, Future, and Hybridized Technologies." Journal of Materials Chemistry A, vol. 7, no. 7,

Chapter 3
Managing Grid Stability and Smart Grids

Noah Serethe

Grid stability management refers to the ability of the electrical grid to keep a balance between energy supply and demand, ensuring that electricity is delivered to customers reliably and safely. Smart grids are a technologically enabled method for 1. guaranteeing grid stability due to the fact they combine cutting-edge sensors, 2. automation, and 3. communication technologies to enable real-time grid monitoring and control. These technologies enable grid resilience improvement, supply and demand balancing, and grid the integration of renewable energy sources. Grid operators may get real-time data on the amount of power being utilized through smart grids. Furthermore, they can enable dynamic pricing of electricity, which can encourage customers to use more power when system demand is reduced.

By integrating sensors, Smart grids contribute to automation, communication, and control systems that can automatically monitor and modify the flow of power on the grid in real-time. This enables it for grid operators to enhance grid efficiency by rapidly adapting to changes in supply and demand. ADR (automated demand response) systems are one approach where smart grids support automation. These systems automatically adjust the consumption of big energy consumers, such as industral or commercial buildings, in response to fluctuations in grid demand, utilizing real-time data on power usage. This may minimize the need for expensive peaking power plants and assist to balance supply and demand. Through including advanced control algorithms that can optimize the production of power plants and other grid assets, smart grids can aid automation. For instance the output of wind and solar power facilities may be optimized using algorithms to make sure they are providing electricity when it is most required. As a result, fewer fossil fuel-based power plants, which are a major source of greenhouse gas emissions, might well be necessary. Overall, by including advanced control algorithms that can optimize the production of power plants and other grid assets, smart grids can assist automation. The output of wind and solar power facilities, for example, may be optimized using algorithms to make sure they are producing electricity when it is most necessary. As a result, less fossil fuel-based power plants which are contributors to a major source of greenhouse gas emissions may very well be necessary. By incorporating communication technologies by integrating cutting edge tech that enable real-time grid monitoring and control, smart grids contribute to communication technology. By providing grid operators access to current knowledge on power requirements and the condition of grid assets, these technologies can assist the grid's improved productivity and reliability. Using sophisticated metering infrastructure is one way smart grids assist with communication technologies (AMI). Smart meters are utilized in this technology that allows real-time communication with the grid and provides grid operators detailed information regarding how much power is used at particular residences and businesses. This information may be utilized to enable dynamic pricing of power and to balance supply and demand. Through the use of intelligent control systems that can automatically detect and alter the flow of power on the grid in real-time, smart grids also assist with communication technologies. These systems automatically modify the output of power plants and other grid assets, ensuring that they are producing energy when it is most necessary, utilizing real-time data on electricity usage and the condition of grid assets. The usage of communication protocols such IEC 61850 and IEC 60870-5-104, which allows systems and devices in the grid to interact with each other quickly and securely, is yet another way that smart grids support communication technologies. This enables the grid to more effectively integrate devices like smart meters, substation automation systems, and renewable energy sources.

Inefficient management of renewable energy sources, such as wind and solar, can make them less predictable and cause grid instability. These sources are frequently decentralized and generate power based on weather conditions. Grid operators must include cutting-edge technology like energy storage systems, demand response, and smart grid controls to overcome this obstacle in order to guarantee stability and dependability. Adding more adaptable conventional power sources, such natural gas power plants, can also aid in balancing out changes in the production of renewable energy and preserving grid stability.

Understanding Grid Stability

It is straightforward: in order for an electrical grid to function properly, production and demand must be balanced. Energy must be generated and consumed in balance in order for stability to exist. In other words, "unreliable" energy sources struggle with traditional grids. Volatility in voltage and frequency disruptions must be responded to for a power grid to stay stable. Imagine, for instance, that there is more energy created than is used or that there is more energy drawn from the grid than is used. The frequency disturbances and power outages then need to be balanced, and this requires complete changes within a reasonable amount of time. The most significant factor is equilibrium.

Renewable Energy into the picture

Between 2019 and 2024, the growth of the renewable energy sector is predicted to soar by a staggering 50%, according to a report from the International Energy Agency (IEA). Leading the pack are solar photovoltaic energy projects, which are quickly gaining traction with the fastest rollouts seen in four years. Wind and hydroelectric projects are following closely behind. Reduced costs for renewable energy technology, globally established targets and decarbonization laws, and rising electricity demand are all contributing to this rise. Grid instability can result from variations in the supply and demand for energy in a specific location when solar energy is used to generate electricity. These variations happen because, for instance, the sunlight intensity in a region where solar-powered homes are common varies from time to time. Thus, while the switch to sustainable energy is ongoing, there will still be periods when the amount of power produced by renewable sources is low, whether it be for homes, offices, or general end consumers. Additionally, if grid operators do not take proper precautions, there may be waste when supply is abundant. Also doing admirably are the wind turbines that are used to generate renewable energy. The grids' stability is still under jeopardy because of the variations in electricity production. The characteristics of wind speed in various applications are what cause these oscillations. Utilizing renewable energy sources is not without its difficulties, which call for firm solutions. These remedies may include methods for storing data, controlling fluctuations, and defining particular resource requirements; (for example, solar power solutions would differ, if not slightly, from solutions for thermal energy sources or hydropower, wind farms, and the rest).

What are the Grid Stability Problems with Renewable Energy Sources

When it comes to integrating renewable energy sources into conventional systems, there are three main obstacles to overcome:

Frequency and Voltage anomalies

The frequency and voltage generated by solar and wind energy production are rather unpredictable due to the random nature of these sources of energy. System variations in the production of solar power are intended to be corrected by power inverters. However, they haven't been very successful in doing this. The time of day and the weather also have an ongoing impact on how much power is produced. The grids' ability to function is significantly impacted by these circumstances, pushing them to their breaking point.

Overloading of existing transmission lines

Due to higher demands during peak hours, it is difficult for the current transmission lines to have capacities that match the intake and outflow of power. When power generators create excessive amounts of power suddenly, the system could go down due to a surge. If the specified capacity of a transmission line is exceeded, thermal loads will accumulate and cause damage.

Demand and supply mismatch

Even if numerous residences, workplaces, and buildings require electricity to function, this cannot be done simultaneously. There are times when the generation of renewable energy might be very high. However, it can also be low in other circumstances. So, when needed, the electricity generated might not be enough or might not match the demand.

How They Can Be solved

Grids using renewable energy can still overcome the challenges they encounter. New technologies that can quickly address these problems are beginning to emerge as a remedy as problems are encountered. Distribution System Operators can restore grid stability by utilizing strategies and technology to guarantee the successful integration of renewable energy in the power industry.

Use of energy storage technologies

To solve the grid stability problems caused by renewable energy, energy storage is an excellent solution. Lithium-ion batteries that are not moving are included, as are batteries that are moving. Energy storage in electric cars using V2G technology is what is meant by the term "moving" batteries. When it comes to battery systems with unique configurations, virtual transmission is one of the technologies that is used. They assist in maintaining the stability of grids by rescuing choked transmission cables.

Implementation of Smart grids

Many features of smart grids collaborate smartly. The control and communication systems are the most beneficial elements that influence grid stability. The sensors can also identify and assess power distribution imbalances. This allows for close monitoring of the equipment's condition. Smart grids can thereby assure grid stability, and Hive Power offers the technologies required for their deployment. Grid managers must constantly monitor the issue of rising renewable energy injections into the grid networks and account for these increases in cost. Operators can also discover answers to problems with grid stability and renewable energy in:

- Developing a massive number of reactive power compensation plants and HVDC transmission connections to connect the generating and load centers
-Utilizing standard load flow controllers (however, these proved to be too slow when compared to the rate at which renewable energy use is growing)
-A unified power flow controller that is capable of quick reactions contains a dynamic load flow management system, which appears to be the ideal choice. By controlling both series and parallel compensation, this approach should keep power lines within the n - 1 criterion balanced, maintaining the best possible flow of electricity.

Types Of Grid Distribution Lines

The several types of distribution lines go from power-generating activities to power transmission, then distribution, and finally consumption. At the distribution level, the network of distribution infrastructure can be based on either an "Overhead" or "Underground" power line configuration depending on a number of factors such as engineering design, budget, technicalities, and legal-technical regulation governing the power market, among others.

Types of Faults on Grid Distribution Lines

following the generation of power and the downstream delivery of the energy to a grid substation over great distances by transmission lines. The grid-substation, distribution substations, and other pertinent power systems and equipment will further distribute and convert power from its current state of high voltage to medium voltage (as required) of various types of grid-connected customers such as homes, businesses, factories, and manufacturers, etc., each with varying load requirements and needs to operate.

Since the distribution of energy currently requires a complex but delicate load-balancing act between power generation, power supply, power distribution, and eventually the management of power consumption, here is where some problems may occur at the distribution-grid level. Since Thomas Edison built the first power grid in New York City more than a century ago, the distribution system has become increasingly complicated and is in desperate need of smarter data-driven and automation technologies, such as renewable energy sources and distributed energy resources (DERs). The conventional power grid and its conventional methods of management are being forced to advance as a result of this as well as rising demands for power consumption.

The implementation and enforcement of international standard policies on all facets of electrical, electronic, and related technologies presents a challenge or, more accurately, an opportunity cost for developing economies, who must choose between focusing their resources and investments on quickly developing crucial power infrastructure. This ought to go hand in hand with one another normally, but it rarely does.

In emerging economies, there is a lack of adherence to international standards, such as those created and published by the International Electro-technical Commission (IEC), which can eventually lead to a number of issues. Before we continue, it is crucial to remember that the IEC's primary goal from the beginning has been to standardize all "electrotechnologies" applications among its members globally by discussing, creating, and publishing standards on issues like, for instance, transmission line design standards, their recommended length, insulation requirements, nominal voltage, and current levels, etc. to vouch for their conformity and, more crucially, that they are safe to operate in their surroundings.

By making sure that their specific energy sectors and the players operating within their framework likewise adhere to these well-known worldwide norms, public power regulatory authorities play a crucial role in this regard. Normally, electricity regulatory authorities within their individual domains of control, or in certain cases, country-wide, are responsible for the enforcement of these requirements.

Unfortunately, this is a problem that frequently affects rapidly developing economies, where it is brought on by a confluence of technical ignorance, the urgent need to build vital public power infrastructure, and insufficient or nonexistent oversight and enforcement of higher technical standards by relevant authorities. Key stakeholders can adopt a coordinated and all-encompassing plan to overcome these challenges by emphasizing the long-term economic and possible risks to the prospects of businesses and human lives resulting from non-adherence to international standards.

Smart Grids

With the introduction of the Smart Grid, the energy sector will enter a new era of dependability, availability, and efficiency that will improve both our economic situation and the environment. To make sure that the advantages we anticipate from the Smart Grid become a reality throughout the transition period, it will be crucial to conduct testing, technology advancements, consumer education, establishment of standards and laws, and information sharing amongst projects. The following are some advantages of the Smart

Grid:
- more effective power transmission
- quicker power restoration following power outages
- reducing operational and administrative costs for utilities, and ultimately lower consumer power bills
- A decrease in peak demand will also aid in lowering electricity prices.
- Integration of large-scale renewable energy systems will increase
- Enhanced customer-owner power generation system integration, particularly that of renewable energy systems
- enhanced security

In the modern world, an interruption in the electrical supply, such as a blackout, can cause a domino effect—a string of failures that can impact banking, communications, traffic, and security. Homeowners may be without heat during the winter, which makes this issue more serious. With more resilience, a smarter grid would strengthen our electrical infrastructure and better position it to handle calamities like hurricanes, earthquakes, huge solar flares, and terrorist attacks. When equipment malfunctions or outages happen, the Smart Grid will enable automatic rerouting thanks to its two-way interactive capability. By doing this, outages will be kept to a minimum, as will their consequences. The use of Smart Grid technology will allow for the isolation and containment of power outages as they happen, preventing them from spreading to cause widespread blackouts. For instance, sending electricity to emergency services first, the new technologies will also ensure that electricity recovery resumes after an emergency in a timely and planned manner. Additionally, when power from utilities is not available, the Smart Grid will make greater use of customer-owned generators to generate power. These "distributed generation" resources can be combined to allow a community to maintain operation of its grocery store, police station, health center, and traffic lights in times of emergency. The Smart Grid also offers a solution for the outdated energy infrastructure that requires modernization or replacement. In order to address energy efficiency and raise consumer knowledge of the link between power use and the environment, this strategy is used. And it's a method to improve national security for our energy system by using more domestic electricity that is more resilient to disasters and attacks.

Smart Grids vs Traditional Grids

The storage capacity of traditional electrical networks was almost nonexistent, and they were hierarchically structured and demand-driven. In order for these different consumers to use the electricity, the voltage in an electricity network is gradually reduced, starting at transmission voltage levels and moving through distribution voltage levels and service voltage levels (in reality, it involves both gearing up and down, making the process a bit more complicated).

Managing a grid is very complex and requires a specialized field for experts who also need to take into account the choices regarding energy regulations and sustainability initiatives by governments. Some of the many challenges that can arise include the effects of extreme weather conditions, damage from wildlife, human sabotage, and other internal and external factors (problems with equipment failure and crucial assets).

The fundamental feature of a smart grid is the two-way flow of electricity and data, which enables it to feed information and data to the various stakeholders in the electricity market. This information and data can be analyzed to optimize the grid, foresee potential issues, react quicker when challenges arise, and build new capacities and services, as the power landscape is changing. The term "smart grid" still refers to the two-way transmission of data and electricity (with prosumers and organizations also producing electricity), but it now has a much broader definition and application because of the numerous opportunities made possible by this significant change and the increasing use of technologies in the context of smart grid deployments.

In conclusion Grid stability is the capacity of an electricity grid to maintain equilibrium between supply and demand for electricity. For the delivery of power to consumers to be trustworthy and secure, this is essential. In order to manage grid stability, smart grids—which integrate digital technology and real-time communication—have become popular. With the use of smart grids, energy usage can be tracked and managed, making it possible to spot and correct imbalances in real time. Additionally, they make it easier to integrate renewable energy sources like wind and solar, which can be unstable and difficult to integrate into conventional networks. Additionally, smart grids can improve overall grid resilience, cut down on energy waste, and increase energy efficiency. However, there are obstacles to integrating smart grid technologies, including high prices and privacy issues.

References

Sher, Omar. "Basics of Distribution Grids & Managing Grid Stability." LinkedIn, 14 October 2022, https://www.linkedin.com/pulse/basics-distribution-grids-managing-grid-stability-omar-sher. Accessed 31 January 2023.

"Smart Grid: The Smart Grid." SmartGrid.gov, https://www.smartgrid.gov/the_smart_grid/smart_grid.html. Accessed 31 January 2023.

"Grid Stability Issues With Renewable Energy Sources: How They Can Be Solved." Hive Power, 22 March 2021, https://www.hivepower.tech/blog/grid-stability-issues-with-renewable-energy-how-they-can-be-solved. Accessed 31 January 2023.

Contributor, Guest. "Managing grid stability in the changing energy landscape." Power Engineering International, 14 October 2020, https://www.powerengineeringint.com/smart-grid-td/td-infrastructure/managing-grid-stability-in-the-changing-energy-landscape/. Accessed 31 January 2023.

Chapter 4
Decentralized Energy Infrastructure

Monsur Moshood

Decentralization refers to the distribution of power and decision-making authority away from a central authority or location. In the context of energy infrastructure, decentralization can refer to the shift from a centralized power generation model, where a single large power plant supplies electricity to a wide area, to a decentralized model where smaller, distributed energy resources are used to generate electricity closer to where it is consumed.

There are several key benefits to decentralization in the energy sector. One major advantage is that it can increase the resilience and reliability of the power grid by reducing the risk of a single point of failure. In a centralized system, a power outage at a single large power plant can disrupt electricity supply to a wide area. In a decentralized system, however, smaller, distributed energy resources can help to mitigate the impact of an outage at any one location (Hiskens, 2016). Decentralization can also increase the efficiency of energy use. In a centralized system, electricity must be transmitted over long distances, which can result in energy losses due to transmission and distribution. In a decentralized system, electricity can be generated closer to where it is consumed, reducing transmission and distribution losses (Strachan, 2014). Another benefit of decentralization is that it can increase the use of renewable energy sources. Centralized power generation is often based on fossil fuels, which can be difficult to access and transport to power plants. Decentralized energy resources, such as solar panels and wind turbines, can be installed closer to where the energy is needed, making it easier to use renewable energy sources (Perez-Arriaga, 2019). Decentralization can also increase energy security. In a centralized system, a disruption to the supply of fossil fuels can cause widespread power outages. In a decentralized system, however, energy can be generated from a variety of sources, making it less vulnerable to disruptions to a single fuel source (Edelman & Keogh, 2016). Additionally, decentralization can also promote community ownership, participation, and empowerment. In a decentralized energy system, communities can play a more active role in decision-making and management of their energy supply, encouraging greater investment in local energy generation and distribution (Jacobs & Palamountain, 2017).

However, decentralization also has its own challenges and limitations. One of the main challenges is the cost of installing and maintaining distributed energy resources. Decentralized systems can be more expensive to install and maintain than centralized systems, which can be a barrier to their widespread adoption (Pachauri, 2015). Additionally, managing and integrating decentralized energy resources into the existing power grid can be complex, and requires significant investments in new technologies and infrastructure. This can be a significant barrier to the widespread adoption of decentralized energy systems, especially in developing countries where there is a lack of infrastructure and funding (Agrawal & Goldemberg, 2018).

In order to establish the avenues for the decentralization of energy infrastructures, we need to examine the most common forms of energy infrastructure.

Power generation infrastructure

Power generation infrastructure refers to the facilities and equipment used to produce electricity. There are several types of power generation, including fossil fuels, nuclear, hydro, wind, solar and more. Fossil fuel power generation is the most common form of power generation and typically uses coal, natural gas, or oil as a fuel source. These power plants burn the fuel to generate heat, which is then used to produce steam to turn turbines and generate electricity (International Energy Agency, 2020). Nuclear power generation uses nuclear reactions to generate heat, which is then used to produce steam to turn turbines and generate electricity. Nuclear power plants are considered as a low-carbon source of electricity, however, they have high investment costs and concerns about nuclear waste disposal and safety (World Nuclear Association, 2020).

Hydroelectric power generation uses the energy of falling water to generate electricity. It is a renewable energy source, and it has a low operating cost and no emissions, however, it often requires large dams which can affect the environment and local communities (Energy Information Administration, 2020). Wind power generation uses wind turbines to generate electricity. It is a renewable energy source with low operating costs and no emissions, however, it depends on wind availability and it can affect the visual aspect of the area (American Wind Energy Association, 2020). Solar power generation uses solar panels to convert the sun's energy into electricity. It is a renewable energy source with low operating costs and no emissions, however, it also depends on weather and daylight conditions (Solar Energy Industries Association, 2020). The decentralization of power generation infrastructure is an important avenue for reducing the environmental impact of energy production. Decentralized power generation infrastructure can reduce the need for large-scale power plants, which are often associated with high levels of air and water pollution. Decentralized power generation infrastructure can also reduce the need for long-distance transmission lines, which can be costly and inefficient. Additionally, decentralized power generation infrastructure can provide more reliable and resilient energy sources, as well as increased energy security. An existing decentralized power generation infrastructure is community solar, which allows individuals to collectively own and benefit from a solar installation. This model has been implemented in states such as Colorado and Minnesota in the United States, and has been shown to increase access to solar power for low-income and disadvantaged communities (Weisbrod & Rabe, 2018).

An avenue for the decentralization of power generation infrastructures is through the use of renewable energy sources, like the aforementioned solar, and wind power. These sources can be easily integrated into decentralized systems, as they can be generated at a small scale and distributed directly to consumers. For example, small-scale solar panels can be installed on individual homes and buildings, allowing residents to generate their own power and reduce their dependence on the grid. Another avenue for decentralization is through the use of microgrids. A microgrid is a local energy system that can operate independently from the main grid, and can include a variety of energy sources such as renewable energy, combined heat and power, and energy storage. Microgrids can provide reliable and resilient power to communities, businesses, and other users in the event of a blackout or other emergency. A third avenue is through peer-to-peer energy trading, which is enabled by blockchain technology. This allows for individual energy producers, such as homeowners with solar panels, to sell excess energy to their neighbors or other consumers, rather than only being able to sell it back to the grid. This creates a more efficient and decentralized energy market, and allows for more active participation from individuals and small businesses in the energy system.

Transmission and distribution infrastructure

Energy transmission and distribution infrastructure refers to the networks of high-voltage power lines and substations that are used to transmit electricity from power plants to homes and businesses. Transmission infrastructure includes the long-distance high-voltage power lines and substations that connect power plants to the larger grid, allowing electricity to be transported over long distances to areas of high demand. These high-voltage lines are typically hundreds of kilometers long and operate at voltage levels of 110 kV or more, reducing energy losses during transmission (National Grid, 2021). Distribution infrastructure includes the lower-voltage power lines and substations that connect the transmission system to homes and businesses. These lines operate at voltage levels of less than 110 kV, and they are responsible for distributing electricity to the final customers. Distribution networks are typically operated by local utilities and are designed to meet the specific needs of the local area (European Network of Transmission System Operators for Electricity, 2020). Transmission and distribution infrastructure is a crucial component of the overall energy system, allowing electricity to be transported over long distances to areas of high demand, and ensuring that electricity is delivered to homes and businesses in a reliable and efficient manner.

However, building and maintaining transmission and distribution infrastructure can be a significant challenge, as it requires significant investment and coordination between different stakeholders such as power generators, transmission and distribution companies, and regulators. Additionally, the expansion of transmission and distribution infrastructure can be met with resistance from local communities and environmentalists, who may be concerned about the environmental impact of new power lines and substations (U.S Energy Information Administration, 2021).

An existing form of decentralized transmission and distribution infrastructure is the use of high-voltage direct current (HVDC) transmission lines, which are more efficient and reliable than traditional alternating current (AC) transmission lines. This technology has been used to transmit electricity generated by wind and solar power plants over long distances and across international borders (Lu and Wang, 2016).

Another method of decentralization could be through the use of distributed energy resources (DERs), such as solar panels, wind turbines, and energy storage. These resources can be connected to the grid at the distribution level, allowing for the decentralization of power generation and transmission. This can lead to more efficient and reliable power systems, as well as increased participation from individuals and small businesses in the energy system. A third avenue for decentralization is through the use of microgrids, which can operate independently from the main grid and can include a variety of energy sources. Microgrids can provide reliable and resilient power to communities, businesses, and other users in the event of a blackout or other emergency, and can also increase the integration of renewable energy sources.

Oil and gas production infrastructure

Oil and gas production infrastructures refer to the facilities and equipment used to extract, process, and transport these resources from their source to the point of consumption. These infrastructures include drilling platforms, pipelines, refineries, storage tanks, and terminals. Drilling platforms are used to extract oil and gas from beneath the earth's surface. These can be offshore or onshore and can be fixed or floating. Pipelines are used to transport the extracted resources over long distances. These can be buried underground or laid on the surface. Refineries process the raw oil and gas into usable products such as gasoline and heating oil. Storage tanks are used to store the processed resources until they are ready to be transported to the point of consumption. Terminals are used to load and unload resources from ships and transport them to other locations.

The construction and maintenance of these infrastructures require significant investment and expertise. The oil and gas industry has faced criticism for potential negative impacts on the environment and local communities. However, these resources remain a vital source of energy for many countries and are expected to continue playing a significant role in the global energy mix for the foreseeable future.

One example of a decentralized oil and gas production infrastructure is shale drilling, which involves the extraction of oil and gas from shale rock formations. This technology has been widely adopted in the United States and has led to a significant increase in domestic oil and gas production (EIA, 2020). Another example is the use of tight oil and tight gas, which are unconventional oil and gas resources that are found in low-permeability rock formations. These resources can be extracted using technologies such as hydraulic fracturing, also known as fracking, and horizontal drilling (EIA, 2019).

The use of advanced drilling and production technologies could be the next step in the decentralization of oil and gas production infrastructures, such as horizontal drilling and hydraulic fracturing. These technologies allow for the extraction of oil and gas from unconventional sources, such as shale rock, and can enable the development of smaller, more decentralized oil and gas production operations. This can lead to more efficient and reliable oil and gas production, as well as increased participation from individuals and small businesses in the energy system.

Refining and processing infrastructure

Refining and processing infrastructures are the facilities and equipment used to convert crude oil and natural gas into usable products such as gasoline, diesel fuel, jet fuel, heating oil, propane, and various chemical feedstocks. These infrastructures include refineries, natural gas processing plants, and petrochemical facilities. Refineries are the primary infrastructure used to process crude oil into various products. They typically include several processing units, such as distillation columns, catalytic cracking units, and hydrocracking units, that separate the different components of crude oil based on their boiling points. The refined products are then transported to storage tanks and terminals for distribution. Natural gas processing plants are used to remove impurities such as water vapor, carbon dioxide, and sulfur compounds from natural gas before it can be transported through pipelines. These plants also separate natural gas liquids (NGLs) such as propane and butane, which are used as fuel or chemical feedstocks. Petrochemical facilities use NGLs and other refined products as feedstocks to produce chemicals such as plastics, fertilizers, and synthetic fibers. These facilities are an important part of the oil and gas industry, as they provide the raw materials for many industrial and consumer products. The refining and processing infrastructures require significant investment and expertise to build and maintain. It also requires strict regulations to ensure safety and to minimize the environmental impact. Existing decentralized refining and processing production infrastructures include the use of micro refineries, which are small-scale refineries that are designed to process lower volumes of feedstock, such as crude oil or natural gas liquids, into refined products such as gasoline, diesel, and jet fuel. Micro refineries can be located closer to the source of the feedstock, reducing transportation costs and increasing the efficiency of the refining process (Microfineries, 2022). Another example is the use of modular refineries, which are prefabricated and pre-tested refinery units that can be quickly and easily assembled and disassembled at the site. This technology can be used to create small-scale refineries in remote or under-served areas, or to process unconventional feedstocks such as heavy oil or oil sands. Decentralized refining and processing can also be incorporated into small-scale chemical plants, which can produce a wide range of chemical products from feedstocks such as natural gas, coal, biomass, and waste materials. These plants can be located closer to the source of the feedstock and can reduce transportation costs, and increase the efficiency of the refining process.

Energy Storage infrastructure

Energy storage infrastructures are facilities and equipment used to store and manage energy for later use. This includes systems that store energy in various forms, such as chemical, mechanical, and thermal. The most common forms of energy storage are batteries and pumped hydroelectric storage. Batteries are widely used to store electrical energy, and they come in various forms such as lead-acid, lithium-ion, and sodium-sulfur. They are used in homes, businesses, and in grid-scale energy storage systems. Grid-scale energy storage systems are designed to store energy generated by renewable energy sources, such as solar and wind power, so that it can be used when the renewable source is not available. Pumped hydroelectric storage is another form of energy storage infrastructure that uses excess electrical energy to pump water from a lower reservoir to an upper reservoir. When the stored energy is needed, the water is released to generate electricity through a hydroelectric turbine. Energy storage infrastructures play a critical role in the transition to a more sustainable energy system by allowing for the integration of renewable energy sources and the management of energy demand. The development and deployment of energy storage technologies are rapidly evolving, and research is ongoing to improve their efficiency and reduce costs.

An avenue for decentralization is through the use of advanced battery storage technologies, such as lithium-ion batteries and flow batteries. These technologies allow for the efficient storage of large amounts of energy at a relatively low cost, and can enable the development of smaller, more decentralized storage operations. This can lead to more efficient and reliable energy storage, as well as increased participation from individuals and small businesses in the energy system. One example of a decentralized energy storage infrastructure is the use of lithium-ion batteries, which are widely used in a variety of applications, including electric vehicles, grid energy storage, and portable electronics. Lithium-ion batteries have high energy density, long cycle life, and low self-discharge rate, making them well-suited for energy storage applications. Another example is the use of lead-acid batteries, which have been widely used in automotive and industrial applications for decades. Lead-acid batteries are relatively inexpensive and have a long service life, making them well-suited for energy storage applications in remote or under-served areas. Decentralized energy storage can also be incorporated into compressed air energy storage (CAES) which store energy in the form of compressed air in underground caverns, which can be used to generate electricity when needed by releasing the compressed air to drive a turbine.

Decentralized energy infrastructures have gained increasing attention in recent years as a way to improve the reliability, efficiency, and sustainability of energy systems. As decentralization refers to the shift away from centralized systems, such as large power plants and transmission and distribution networks, towards smaller, more distributed systems that are closer to the point of consumption. By decentralizing energy infrastructures, a more resilient, flexible, and sustainable energy system can be achieved.

Power generation infrastructures are one of the key areas where decentralization can be implemented. Instead of relying on large centralized power plants, decentralized systems such as distributed solar and wind power can be integrated into the grid. This not only increases the diversity of energy sources, but also allows for greater participation from individuals and small businesses in the energy system. This can also lead to a more resilient and reliable power system, as distributed energy resources can continue to function even if the main grid is down.

Transmission and distribution infrastructures are also an important area for decentralization. By connecting distributed energy resources directly to the distribution network, the need for large, centralized transmission and distribution systems can be reduced. This not only improves the efficiency of the energy system, but also increases the resilience of the power grid and reduces the risk of outages.

Oil and gas production infrastructures can also benefit from decentralization. Instead of relying on large, centralized oil and gas fields, smaller, distributed resources can be developed. This not only increases the diversity of energy sources, but also allows for greater participation from individuals and small businesses in the energy system. Additionally, distributed oil and gas production can be more efficient and sustainable as it reduces the need for long-distance transportation.

Refining and processing infrastructures are also an important area for decentralization. By locating refining and processing facilities closer to the point of production, the need for long-distance transportation of raw materials can be reduced. This not only improves the efficiency of the energy system, but also reduces the environmental impact of energy production. Additionally, it allows for greater participation from individuals and small businesses in the energy system.

Storage infrastructures are also an important area for decentralization. Instead of relying on large, centralized storage systems, decentralized systems such as advanced battery storage technologies and microgrids can be integrated into the energy system. This not only increases the diversity of energy storage options, but also allows for greater participation from individuals and small businesses in the energy system. Additionally, decentralized storage can be more efficient and sustainable as it reduces the need for long-distance transportation of energy. Overall, decentralization of energy infrastructures can provide a number of benefits and open new avenues for the integration of advanced technologies and other distributed energy resources. The implementation of these ideas and technologies is still in its early stages, but it's expected to gain more traction in the future as the need for more sustainable and reliable energy systems continues to grow.

References

"Decentralized energy systems for sustainable energy access," by I. Hiskens, 2016.

"Decentralized Energy Systems: Economic and Environmental Benefits" by P. Strachan, 2014.

"Decentralized Renewable Energy for Rural Development," by L. Perez-Arriaga, 2019.

"Decentralized Energy Systems and the Law," by J. Edelman and G. Keogh, 2016.

"Decentralized Energy Systems: Community-Based Approaches," by D. Jacobs and M. Palamountain, 2017.

"The Economics of Decentralized Energy Systems," by R. Pachauri, 2015.
"Decentralized Energy Systems in Developing Countries," by A. Agrawal and D. Goldemberg, 2018.

Weisbrod, G., & Rabe, B. G. (2018). Community solar in the United States: Current status and future prospects. Energy Policy, 116, 225-234.

"Decentralized Energy Systems" by Sabine Fuss, Thomas Hamacher, and Stefanie Lohaus

"Microgrids and Other Distributed Energy Resources" by National Renewable Energy Laboratory

"Blockchain for Decentralized Energy Systems" by Christoph Burger, Ingo Stadler, and Florian Dörr

"Fossil Fuel Power Generation," by International Energy Agency, 2020.
Lu, X., & Wang, X. (2016). The development and prospects of HVDC transmission technology. Renewable and Sustainable Energy Reviews, 54, 1272-1285.

"Decentralized Energy Systems" by Sabine Fuss, Thomas Hamacher, and Stefanie Lohaus.

"Microgrids and Other Distributed Energy Resources" by National Renewable Energy Laboratory.

"Smart Grid Technologies: Advanced Metering Infrastructure (AMI)" by US Department of Energy.

"Distributed Energy Resources" by Sandia National Laboratories.

"Microgrids for Reliable and Resilient Energy Systems" by IEEE Power and Energy Society.
"Nuclear Power in the World Today," by World Nuclear Association, 2020.

"Hydropower," by Energy Information Administration, 2020.

"Wind Power," by American Wind Energy Association, 2020.

"Solar Power," by Solar Energy Industries Association, 2020.

Lu, X., & Wang, X. (2016). The development and prospects of HVDC transmission technology. Renewable and Sustainable Energy Reviews, 54, 1272-1285.

"Decentralized Energy Systems" by Sabine Fuss, Thomas Hamacher, and Stefanie Lohaus.

"Microgrids and Other Distributed Energy Resources" by National Renewable Energy Laboratory.

"Smart Grid Technologies: Advanced Metering Infrastructure (AMI)" by US Department of Energy.

"Distributed Energy Resources" by Sandia National Laboratories.

"Microgrids for Reliable and Resilient Energy Systems" by IEEE Power and Energy Society.

"Transmission and Distribution," by National Grid, 2021.

"Distribution Networks," by European Network of Transmission System Operators for Electricity, 2020.

"Transmission and Distribution Challenges," by U.S Energy Information Administration, 2021.

EIA. (2020). Shale gas and tight oil. Retrieved from https://www.eia.gov/energyexplained/oil-and-petroleum/shale-gas-and-tight-oil.

US Energy Information Administration. (2019). Unconventional Oil and Gas. Retrieved from https://www.eia.gov/energyexplained/oil-and-petroleum/unconventional-oil-and-gas.

"Decentralized Energy Systems" by Sabine Fuss, Thomas Hamacher, and Stefanie Lohaus.

"Shale Gas and Tight Oil: The U.S. Experience" by the U.S. Energy Information Administration.

"Distributed Energy Resources" by Sandia National Laboratories. "Microgrids for Reliable and Resilient Energy Systems" by IEEE Power and Energy Society.

"Combined Heat and Power (CHP) for Distributed Energy Systems" by the U.S. Department of Energy.

Microrefineries: Small Scale Refineries for Crude Oil, Naphtha, Gasoline, Diesel, Kerosene, Jet Fuel and Specialty Products. (2022). Microrefineries.org. Retrieved from https://microrefineries.org/

Modular Refineries. (2022). ModularRefineries.com. Retrieved from https://modularrefineries.com.

Small Scale Chemical Plants. (2022). SmallScaleChemicalPlants.com. Retrieved from https://smallscalechemicalplants.com.

Energy Storage Association. (2022). Lithium-Ion Batteries. Retrieved from https://energystorage.org/technology/lithium-ion-batteries.

Lead Acid Battery Consortium. (2022). Lead-Acid Batteries

Chapter 5
Residual Heat Distribution in Aircraft Systems

Christina Nguyen

Summary: Aircraft engines produce energy to power flight, but they can also burn fuel inefficiently. Much of the energy produced is released as heat outside of the airplane system, which is inefficient if not recovered for another use. This article discusses heat recovery in aircraft systems from a practical point of view, offering several possible solutions that are being explored in the industry, as seen in the literature. It also defines some technical terms and concepts, bringing in parallel fields' findings, and provides a good overview of each solution.

1. The overheating problem in aircraft systems

In both turbine aircraft and reciprocating (piston) aircraft engines, having excessive heat is detrimental to the operation of the aircraft and to safety. There must always be a means to control or to eliminate excessive heat, lest there be major damage to components, detonation, knocking, or even an engine failure. Excess energy harvesting could also potentially result in cost savings for both manufacturers and airline businesses in the context of the aviation sector. In fact, it might lower the price of producing cables and customizing planes. There are several common ways of removing that excessive heat. For a reciprocating aircraft engine that usually means using air to remove the heat with circulation, though some light aircrafts are using diesel liquid to cool the engines. Again, in the case of liquid diesel, the liquid circulates around the area generating heat (the engine), absorbing the heat and then dissipating it safely away to another area (e.g. outside the plane) using a heat exchanger or radiator. For turbine engines, air flow is used to cool the components, see figure 1 for an example of this case.

Unfortunately, cooling systems are not making the most efficient use of that excess heat that issiphoned off of the overheating engine systems. The heat is generally redirected outside of the aircraft, when it could be used back in the powerplant system to generate different types of useful power. In the next sections of this paper, we will discuss one inefficient way currently used, and then several possible solutions to recapture that heat in a useful way.

2. Not the most efficient way: the reciprocating engine cooling system

a. What they are, how they work

75 gallons of water may be boiled with just one gallon of aviation fuel. It is therefore simple to understand that an engine that burns roughly 4 liters of fuel every minute produces a significant amount of heat. Generally, only a quarter of the heat that is released is converted into usable power. To prevent it from damaging the engine, the remaining heat must be expelled. In a normal airplane powerplant, the engine absorbs half of the heat and releases the other half as exhaust. Circulating oil transfers some of the heat absorbed by the engine to the airstream via the oil cooler. The remainder is handled by the engine cooling system. Transferring the surplus heat from the cylinders to the air is the process of cooling, however cooling involves more than just putting the cylinders in the airstream ("Aircraft Reciprocating Engine Cooling Systems and Maintenance" n.d.).

Though an engine's cylinder may be small relative to the whole airframe (for example, in general aviation aircraft), its outer surface area can be increased (to better shed heat) using "cooling fins." Cooling fins are protrusions from the main shell of the engine cylinder (which is, of course, shaped like a cylinder) that look very like the fins on a fish. In this way, the shape of the cylinder is more like a ridged barrel, and this arrangement means that heat is transferred by radiation. Fins play an integral role in helping to dispose of the heat; so if the cooling fin is broken off of the cylinder, the cylinder can overheat in a particular location (called a "hotspot"), leading to significant engine damage and serious safety risks (e.g. malfunctioning equipment or even engine failure). So, to prevent this, cylinders have a minimum amount of fins they must have before needing to be replaced ("Aircraft Reciprocating Engine Cooling Systems).

The purpose of the cowling and baffles is to push air over the cylinder cooling fins. The air is forced close around the cylinders by the baffles (as a jacket), which also prevent heated, stagnant air pools from accumulating when the main streams pass by unimpeded. To avoid overheating of the ignition leads, blast tubes are incorporated into the baffles to deliver jets of cooling air onto the back spark plug elbows of each cylinder. There are components called "blast tubes" built directly into the baffles to direct jets of cooling air to a section of the cylinders called "the rear spark plug" (i.e. the place where ignition leads are, which need to not experience overheating) ("Aircraft Reciprocating Engine Cooling Systems and Maintenance" n.d.).

It is possible for an engine to operate at a temperature that is too low. An engine maintains its operating temperature during flight for the same reasons it is warmed up before takeoff. An engine must be maintained at its ideal operating temperature to ensure proper fuel distribution, evaporation, and oil circulation. Airflow over the engine is regulated by temperature controls on the aircraft engine. The engine may overheat during takeoff and become excessively cold at high-altitude, high-speed, and low-power letdowns if controls are not supplied ("Aircraft Reciprocating Engine Cooling Systems and Maintenance" n.d.).

"Cowl flaps," a method with little risk, are the most typical method of managing cooling (see figure 2 below). In some light aircraft, manual operation is used to open and close these flaps instead of hydraulic actuators or electric motor-driven jackscrews ("How It Works: Cowl Flaps - AOPA" n.d.). The cowl flaps create drag and give up streamlining when they are extended for increased cooling . The cowl flaps are just slightly opened before takeoff in order to keep the engine's temperature below the danger zone. So that drag is as minimal as feasible, heating above the usual range is permitted (introducing some minimal risk). The cowl flaps should be opened widely during ground operations because drag is unimportant and cooling should be maximized. Most older aircraft and radial engine installations feature cowl flaps for cooling("How It Works: Cowl Flaps - AOPA" n.d.) .

Older (not modern) aircrafts also use augmentors to add even more cooling airflow ("Augmentor Tube(s) -" n.d.). There are two sets of tubes in each

nacelle that connect the rear of the nacelle to the engine compartment. The inner augmentor tubes receive exhaust gas from the exhaust collectors.
An exhaust with a high temperature and low pressure (like a jet) is created when the exhaust gas combines with air that has passed over the engine. The augmentors' low-pressure region draws more cooling air over the engine. Through contact with the augmentor tubes, air entering the augmentors' outer shells is heated, but it is not tainted with exhaust gasses. The heating, defrosting, and anti-icing system in the aircraft cabin receives hot air from the shell ("Augmentor Tube(s) -" n.d.).

Augmentors work by using exhaust gas velocity to produce airflow over the engine, and so cooling is not entirely dependent on a prop wash ("Augmentor Tube(s) -" n.d.). The volume of air can be controlled by vanes that are attached to the augmenters; they can be adjusted but usually are left in the "trail" position to allow the most flow possible (and maximum cooling). Sometimes, they may be left in the closed position to increase the heat in the cabin, to de-ice (by melting the ice on the surface), or to prevent the engine from over-cooling during descents from high altitudes. Furthermore, as a complement to the augmentors system, some aircrafts have residual heat doors to let the extra heat escape after engines are shut down ("Augmentor Tube(s) -" n.d.).

b. Checking up on the cylinder temperature with indicating systems
An indicator, electrical wire, and a thermocouple are typically used in this technique of checking cylinder temperatures (with indicating systems). The instrument and the nacelle firewall are connected by wiring. The other end of the thermocouple leads is connected to the cylinder at the firewall, while the other end is connected to the electrical wire. A thermocouple is an instrument made of two metals that are dissimilar in their physical properties, especially constanton and iron, and they are connected by wiring to an indication system (i.e. a system that can read the metals). The indicator tells us that if the temperature of the junction is much different from the temperature at the intersection of metal-to-wire, there will be a voltage. The presence of the voltage means that a current is sent through wires to the indicator, which is a current-measuring tool ("Aircraft Temperature Measuring Instruments" n.d.). Either a bayonet or a gasket kind of thermocouple end connects to the cylinder.

The knurled nut is pressed down and rotated clockwise until it is snug to install the bayonet type. This type's removal involves pushing down on the nut and turning it anticlockwise until it releases. The type of gasket sits beneath the spark plug and takes the place of the standard spark plug gasket ("Aircraft Temperature Measuring Instruments" n.d.). The thermocouple is engineered to provide a specific level of resistance. A false temperature reading is obtained if the lead's length is decreased. As established by the block test, the thermocouple's bayonet or gasket is inserted or placed on the engine's hottest cylinder. The cylinder temperature is displayed when the thermocouple is mounted and the instrument's wiring is linked. The cylinder head temperature indicator displays the free outside air temperature prior to starting the engine, provided that the engine is at ambient temperature. This is one way to check if the instrument is in good working order ("Aircraft Temperature Measuring Instruments" n.d.).

Regular checks should be made to ensure that the cylinder head temperature indicator's cover glass has not slipped or fractured. To check, one should look for any signs of missing or broken decals that indicate temperature restrictions on the cover glass. The tie should be checked for security or wire chafing (e.g. indentations where the wire rubbed against the material) if the thermocouple leads had to be coiled and tied down due to their excessive length. Check the bayonet or gasket for cleanliness and mounting security. The electrical connections should all be examined while the engine is running if the cylinder head temperature pointer changes.

c. Checking up on the exhaust gas's temperature with indicating systems
A thermocouple is positioned in the exhaust stream immediately after the cylinder port to serve as the exhaust gas temperature indicator. The instrument in the instrument panel is then connected to it. This enables the mixture to be adjusted, which has a significant impact on engine temperature. The engine temperature may be managed and watched by using this instrument to set the mixture ("Exhaust Gas Temperature (EGT) | SKYbrary Aviation Safety" n.d.).

3. Solutions overviews

a. Heat exchangers: in this case, heat is transferred from one fluid to another by use of heat exchangers. Heat exchangers can be used in airplanes to transfer heat from exhaust gas to another fluid, such as water or engine oil. The hot fluid can subsequently be used to create electricity or heat the cabin, among other valuable tasks (Xu et al. 2020).

b. Rankine cycle systems: Rankine cycle systems are utilized to convert heat into electricity. They are already popularly used in other industrial areas with excellent outcomes, like nuclear reactors (where the heat from the radiation is turned into electricity). They function by converting heat into mechanical work by absorbing it through a fluid, such as water or a specific working fluid. A generator is then powered by the mechanical work to generate electricity. What is especially promising in this case is that heat can be recovered from the exhaust gas (gas that would otherwise just flow into the outside air while still having usable heat energy) of an airplane's engines using Rankine cycle technology.

c. Thermoelectric generators: Thermoelectric generators (TEGs) are machines that produce usable electricity by using the temperature difference between two materials (i.e. a warmer and cooler material). Generally speaking, the difference between the materials produces a current flow (electricity); the magnitude of this temperature difference is directly related to the amount of voltage difference in the thermoelectric generator's circuit; likewise, the direction of heat flow determines the polarity of the voltage. TEGs can be used to capture an engine's waste heat and transform it into usable electricity before it even becomes exhaust gas (longer explanation of this below, with images). These solutions are still in development and have not been perfected for aviation use yet, though they are very promising ("More Juice, Fewer Emissions: Towards Greener Power Devices | CHALLENGE Project | Results in Brief | H2020 | CORDIS | European Commission" n.d.; "Aircraft Energy Recovery System Reduces Fuel Consumption | RENERGISE Project | Results in Brief | FP7 | CORDIS | European Commission" n.d.).

d. Combustion turbine generators: In this case, like inside a typical combustion turbine engine, we can use the combustion turbine method again to create electricity from waste heat simply by placing the generator in a way where it can capture the exhaust gas from the engines (i.e. getting energy twice from the same fuel using the same method.) Combustion turbine generators can be used to generate energy by burning fuel in a turbine; the heat generated by the burning fuel is used to produce steam, which will then power the turbine to produce usable electricity.

4. Possible solution #1: spotlight on the thermoelectric generator

Thermoelectric generators depend on the "Seebeck Effect," which creates an electrical current when dissimilar metals (like mentioned above in the summary) are at two different temperatures. The Seebeck Effect therefore allows heat to turn into useful electricity, and is a relatively straightforward application. The voltage produced by the TEGs (Seebeck generators) is directly related to the temperate difference between the dissimilar metals ("What Is the Seebeck Effect?" n.d.).

Generally, thermoelectric generators use electricity to produce heating and cooling, and so are called "solid-state heat engines". The two dissimilar metals are specifically pairs of p-type and n-type elements. (In n-type, the electrons have a negative charge, hence the name n-type. In p-type, the effect of a positive charge is created in the absence of an electron, hence the name p-type. See the image above). Both metals are semiconductor materials.

To generate electricity, the mobile holes in the p-type element "see" the mobile electrons in the n-type element when they are electrically connected to one other, and they move to the opposite side of the junction (in an attempt to equalize the charges). An electron from the n-type element migrates into the p-type element for every hole that enters the n-type element. It takes a very short time for each hole and electron to "swap sides," to reach equilibrium, and to operate as a barrier to stop further electron or "hole" migration. The "depletion zone" is what this is called, and the current has been generated ("What Is the Seebeck Effect?" n.d.).

5. Possible solution #2: spotlight on the Rankine cycle system

Power plants that employ coal or nuclear energy frequently use the Rankine cycle, also known as the Rankine Vapor Cycle. Fuel is used in this mechanism to generate heat in a boiler, turning water into steam that expands via a turbine to provide useful work. Of course, in airplane systems, this means that extra water will need to be brought up simply for the Rankine system, which may be a disadvantage when compared to other heat-electricity conversion methods (Pateropoulos, Efstathiadis, and Kalfas 2021). William J.M. Rankine, a Scottish engineer, created this method in 1859. This thermodynamic cycle changes heat into mechanical energy, which is often converted by electrical generation into electricity (Pateropoulos, Efstathiadis, and Kalfas 2021).

The cycle works through 4 major components:
- Pump: a pump compresses the fluid to a high pressure (which takes 'work', i.e. some initial input energy)
- Boiler: the fluid that the pump has compressed is heated in the boiler to a very high temperature, so that a phase change occurs to vapor (gas). This is similar to how a steam engine works.
- Turbine: the turbine allows the vapor to expand, which pushes work out (e.g. turning some component).
- Condenser: the vapor condenses in the condenser, and the waste heat goes into the final heat sink (e.g. it can be pushed into the atmosphere or some large body of water).

The high heat of the fluid's vaporization limits the Rankine cycle's efficiency. Water is the most practicable fluid for this cycle because the fluid must be continuously recycled. The waste heat is the reason so many power plants are situated next to a body of water, like a lake or river (Pateropoulos, Efstathiadis, and Kalfas 2021). In the case of airplane systems, this is further proof that there are considerable downsides to using Rankine to manage heat, as the plane must carry that water until it lands, using a potentially unsustainable amount of fuel just to carry that water's weight.

Waste heat is released as water vapor, which is visible blowing from a plant's cooling towers, when the water condenses in the condenser. Any thermodynamic cycle needs this waste heat. This condensation process lowers the pressure at the turbine exit. Because of this, the pump can compress the water with less effort, resulting in improved overall efficiency.

Conclusion

In sum, saving excess heat generated by airplane engines during flight is both cost-efficient and prevents damage to the system. There are multiple theoretical ways for improving the efficiency of any energy flowing, including (but not being limited to) heat exchangers, Rankine cycle systems, thermoelectric generators, and combustion turbine engines. In future, research will be conducted to create innovations in materials and engineering designs; efficient aircraft engines with lower fuel consumption and emissions will be developed for more environmentally friendly air travel at low costs.

References

"Aircraft Energy Recovery System Reduces Fuel Consumption | RENERGISE Project | Results in Brief | FP7 | CORDIS | European Commission." n.d. Accessed January 10, 2023. https://cordis.europa.eu/article/id/180938-aircraft-energy-recovery-system-reduces-fuel-consumption.

"Aircraft Reciprocating Engine Cooling Systems and Maintenance." n.d. Accessed January 12, 2023. https://www.aircraftsystemstech.com/2017/04/engine-cooling-systems.html.

"Aircraft Temperature Measuring Instruments." n.d. Accessed January 8, 2023. https://www.aircraftsystemstech.com/2017/05/instrument-system-temperature-measuring.html.

"Augmentor Tube(s) -." n.d. Accessed January 8, 2023. http://www.avcanada.ca/forums2/viewtopic.php?t=50507.

"Exhaust Gas Temperature (EGT) | SKYbrary Aviation Safety." n.d. Accessed January 10, 2023. https://www.skybrary.aero/articles/exhaust-gas-temperature-egt.

"How It Works: Cowl Flaps - AOPA." n.d. Accessed January 12, 2023. https://www.aopa.org/news-and-media/all-news/2017/november/flight-training-magazine/how-it-works-cowl-flaps.

"More Juice, Fewer Emissions: Towards Greener Power Devices | CHALLENGE Project | Results in Brief | H2020 | CORDIS | European Commission." n.d. Accessed January 12, 2023. https://cordis.europa.eu/article/id/430470-more-juice-fewer-emissions-towards-greener-power-devices.

Pateropoulos, G. E., T. G. Efstathiadis, and A. I. Kalfas. 2021. "Organic Rankine Cycle for Turboprop Engine Application." The Aeronautical Journal 125 (1291): 1666–86. https://doi.org/10.1017/AER.2021.32.

"What Is the Seebeck Effect?" n.d. Accessed January 10, 2023. https://www.techtarget.com/searchnetworking/definition/Seebeck-effect.

Xu, Yihao, Hailong Tang, Min Chen, and Fei Duan. 2020. "Optimization and Design of Heat Recovery System for Aviation." Applied Thermal Engineering 165 (January): 114581. https://doi.org/10.1016/J.APPLTHERMALENG.2019.114581.

Chapter 6
Combined Heat and Power

Faith Grace Robes

Introduction

Climate change worsens as harmful greenhouse gasses are constantly being pumped into the air. The increasing carbon dioxide emissions for generating power and heat, necessities to fuel human daily living, is killing the sole habitable planet known to humankind day by day. Worldwide carbon dioxide emissions from burning fossil fuels for energy consumption creates 34 billion tonnes annually ("Carbon Dioxide Emissions From Electricity"). While it is impossible to cut off the use of energy as it is an essential necessity that helps humans live, it is, however, possible to alter the method of generating that energy. One possible solution to the reduction of fossil fuels is co-generation, a more sustainable method which combines both heat and power. In fact, with scientists' emphasizing the need to be more environmentally cautious, various industrialized countries have made it their top priority for sustainability. Moreover, an increasing global population means a direct increase in energy demand. Therefore, replacing traditional power generations to achieve environmental protection while still achieving energy security became the main sustainability focus for many developed countries like the US, China, and Europe (Bórawski et al.).

It has been a great struggle to find various alternative sustainable sources of energy production that are clean, efficient, reliable and affordable for the general public. However, this changed when combined heat and power was first introduced at the beginning of the 20th century as a prospect for an alternative energy source. Engineers first discovered that the waste heat from generating power could be used and stored to supply thermal energy, warmth, to residents in the winter or it can be used for industrial manufacturing (Knowles). Thus, the birth of the combined heat and power principle, also known as the cogeneration system, garnered the attention of many. In fact, this system has been used in essential industries, large employers, urban centers, and campuses in the US– and operates at a 65% to 75% efficiency, compared to the 50% efficiency traditional systems provide ("Combined Heat and Power Basics").

What the combined heat and power system is used for

Prior to exploring the details of the combined heat and power system, the purpose of these systems should be understood. The combined heat and power system integrates a series of technologies to allow for a simultaneous on-site production of electricity and heat ("Combined Heat and Power (CHP) and District Energy"). This system is used to generate power for hospitals, airports, and other large facilities. Combined heat and power systems can provide district heating by using unused steam to produce additional power. Moreover, if this system is implemented in industrial manufacturing plants, this will allow large energy-consuming industries to produce their own stable supply of electricity while increasing their efficiency and decreasing their fuel consumption. In commercial buildings, this system can provide clean power that meets baseload requirements with a reduced energy cost. Again, the steam from the system can provide heating and cooling, while generating electricity for lights and technology. The combined heat and power system can also be used in institutions like universities, hospitals, military bases, and prisons to significantly lower electrical costs all while decreasing harmful emissions. For example, a combined heat and power system is used to power the Texas Medical Center in Houston. This switch increased the hospital's efficiency from 42% to 80%, cut fossil fuel consumption by 61%, and reduced carbon dioxide emissions by more than 305,000 tons every year. Not only did the hospital contribute to lowering greenhouse gas emissions, they were also able to save more than $200 million over fifteen years. In addition to providing energy-intensive institutions, combined heat and power systems can power multiple residential buildings like apartments or single-family houses ("Combined heat and power generation"). It is greatly evident that combined heat and power systems have the capacity and efficiency to benefit the community economically and environmentally.

How the combined heat and power system works
Combined heat and power system is the simultaneous production of electricity using mechanical power and thermal energy from one source of energy ("Combined Heat and Power Basics"). This system is known to be energy efficient because of its capability of generating power and heat from a single source of fuel. Cogeneration systems allow for thermal energy waste to be recovered to produce another form of energy or product (Bagherian). It does not consist of a single form of technology but is a large energy system made up of individual components that work together to produce electricity and make heat that can be stored and used for other purposes ("Combined heat and power generation").

Combined heat and power uses a type of distributed generation wherein the system is located at or near the area of consumption ("Combined Heat and Power Basics").

Gu and colleagues explained that the combined heat and power system is divided into two parts consisting of the power supply loop and the heat supply loop. The fuel cell and heat recovery boiler operate on natural gas as their energy source. The waste heat from the fuel cell through the heat recovery boiler is then recovered to supply to the thermal load. Therefore, achieving the recycling of waste heat as an optimal source of generating power (Gu et al.).

Importance of combined heat and power systems
As society continues to rely on fossil fuels to generate power, society also continues to contribute to the irreversible destruction of the only habitable planet known to humankind. Fossil fuels have a chokehold on humans' operational activities, and it is difficult for people to turn away from this energy resource. Unfortunately, the effects of climate change worsens day by day as humans continue to use fossil fuel generated electricity. In fact, fossil fuels are the largest contributor to climate change globally, as they account for more than 75% of greenhouse gas emissions and almost 90% of all carbon dioxide emissions (United Nations). As mentioned in previous and imminent chapters, what needs to change is the way humans obtain their energy resource. This can be done through the switch to renewable energy resources. Renewable

energy resources can redefine the energy landscape as many engineers and large industries consider using combined heat and power systems their conventional form of generating power. This system in particular offers considerable environmental benefits all while remaining economically friendly. Due to the nature of the design, the captured heat that would in other ways be wasted in other forms of electricity production, will be re-used to produce the same amount of energy and supply the same, if not more power. Combined power and power systems can reduce carbon emissions by up to 30% compared to other means of conventional electrical generation like boilers and power stations. It also has an efficiency of over 80%. Moreover, economically speaking, operators can save 20% on their energy bills (Government of the United Kingdom).

Current implementations: an integrated network of systems

There are several studies indicating the sole use of combined heat and power systems in household environments. It is evident that the use of this system is extremely beneficial to one's economic stance and most importantly, the environment. However, one literature review examined the implementation of combined heat and power system units with other forms of renewable energy resources like solar energy, geothermal energy, and wind energy (Bagherian & Mehranzamir). Another study outlined how the micro-combined heat and power unit can work in conjunction with solar powered systems, including photovoltaic and thermal systems, for domestic environments. Using a lithium-ion battery storage and hot water tank for heat storage, along with the micro combined heating and power unit, the study showed that there is an incredible increase in the system's reliability and independence from the fluctuating climate conditions. It showed that this system supplies over 75% of the total energetic demand of an average household while still reducing more than a third of the carbon dioxide emissions used to produce the consumed energy in the system. With a doubled increase in the system's battery capacity, the system is expected to function completely autonomously. Thermal energy balance generated enough energy to provide space for heating and cooling and hot water (Auñón-Hidalgo et al.).

Gas turbine based CHPs

It is known that the gas turbine is cost-effective and more "environmentally-friendly" than the rest of the fossil fuels as gas turbines burn natural gas. However, despite gas turbines using the "cleaner" energy resource of the fossil fuels, these turbines still consume fossil fuel and partake in further carbon dioxide emissions. Nevertheless, it is important to consider the different forms of combined heat system analyses amongst all forms of implemented networks of systems. Gas turbines are in fact one of the most widely used primary movers for combined heat and power systems for industrial, domestic and power plant energy generation. There are two forms of turbines used for these systems including large scale turbines and microscale turbines. Several studies focus on the exergy efficiency of combined heat and power systems with different forms of turbines such as large-scale and micro-scale (Mahian et al.). Exergy is the amount of work a system can perform when brought into thermodynamic equilibrium with its environment (Jørgensen & Svirezhev). The importance of investigating exergy efficiency is because it gives a finer understanding of the system's performance by highlighting the losses and internal irreversibilities assessed to improve performance (Dincer & Abu-Rayash).

Large scale gas turbines

A very critical issue with combined heat and power systems is its exergy efficiency. One study outlined that over eighty percent of the total exergy destruction happened in the combustion chamber.

Microscale gas turbines

One of the most severe options for creating a decentralized energy generation is using a micro-gas turbine combined heat and power plant due to its great power unit for building blocks. Lately, there has been great attention towards these systems and much research has been conducted to examine its exergy efficiency. One study investigated the exergy analysis for micro gas turbine combined heat and power systems and revealed that the exergy efficiency was almost thirty-six percent.

It has been concluded that there needs to be more ways to improve exergy efficiency in combined heat and power systems as most of the exergy destruction occurred in boiler parts, combustion chambers, and heat exchangers (Mahian et al., 2020). Thus, to improve the efficiency engineers must focus on improving these parts of the system.

Reciprocating internal combustion engine with combined heat and power systems

Many are familiar with the term "Otto engines" and "Diesel engines" used in many applications. These categories stem from the reciprocating internal combustion engines. While the concepts of those two categories are very similar, the ultimate difference is the ignition– as otto engines use spark for their ignition after compressing the fuel, and diesel engines use a self-ignition concept (Martinez et al.).

Exergy analysis in Otto engines

While the average use of otto cycles are used for car engines, many combined heat and power units can also obtain the benefits of otto cycles for their prime movers. Studies have shown that the exergy efficiency is close to twenty-six percent.

Exergy analysis in diesel engines

Diesel cycle engines work by compressing air and atomized diesel fuel injected into the cylinder for spontaneous ignition. Due to the old nature of this mechanism, there has been ample research conducted regarding diesel engines. One of which highlights that the overall exergy efficiency is almost fifty percent. It can be seen that most of the exergy destruction occurred in the combustion process of the system.

As a result, the exergy efficiency for most internal combustion engines in combined heat and power systems are reported to be between 25 to 35%. It is therefore recommended that the addition or replacement of more efficient components would increase the system's exergy efficiency.

Rankine cycle based combined heat and power systems

The Rankine cycle includes the boiler and steam turbine. These are used in conjunction with the combined heat and power applications, and are becoming popular for engineers due to increased exergetic and environmental efficiencies. In addition, the Rankine cycle based combined heat and power systems can be integrated with desalination or solar plants, to improve its performance and efficiency (Mahian et al.).

Fuel cell-powered combined heat and power systems

Fuel cells are electrochemical cells that use hydrogen fuel in the anode to make chemical oxidation (addition of oxygen molecules). Through an electrochemical reaction between oxygen and hydrogen, chemical energy from the process is converted into electrical energy. After several studies conducted analyzing the exergonic analysis in solid oxide, molten-carbonate, and proton exchange membrane fuel cells, it has been suggested that engineers focus on developing other high temperature fuel cells including protonic ceramic fuel cells and direct carbon fuel cells (Martinez et al.).

Combined Heat and Power Systems' Experimental Simulation

A study conducted by Gu and colleagues (2010) created a simulated experiment to investigate the economic operation of cogeneration systems.

Using battery

Since batteries can be charged using redundant power and can be discharged, combined heat and power systems can reduce the amount of power obtained from the main grid, thereby decreasing operating costs.

Using battery and considering peak-valley price

Peak-valley is a term used to describe the highs and lows of electrical usage throughout the year. During peak times, the combined heat and power system cannot meet the power demand and would require purchasing power from the main grid. This purchase is expensive. In the intermediate and valley periods, the excess power is sold to the main grid and the price is low. Granted the power and heat demand curves are not changed, the operation costs will increase compared to solely considering using a battery.

6.3 Synthetic fuel considerations

This model considers the method of peak load shifting to make the resource more effective and reduce operation costs. This resulted in a reduction by 2.5% and is seen as the most effective method of reducing total economic costs, which is greatly beneficial for residential communities as combined heat and power systems are typically used for residential power generators. Moreover, as smart grid technology continues to develop, these technological devices will be able to control home appliances and help users reduce the electricity costs especially during peak electrical prices. Therefore, this option is the most economic and environmentally friendly method of the three considered (Gu et al.).

Future implications and steps

Every time a person decides to consume energy whether it be from turning on the lights to driving a car, one must greatly consider how they are impacting the environment. This is due to the fact that the energy being provided is sourced from burning fossil fuels. Imagine a world where humans and all of nature's creations can live abundantly in harmony with Earth. A place where the consequences of climate warming are no longer of immense concern. An era where humans no longer rely on carbon and the burning of fossil fuels to generate power for everyday living. A future where the air breathed is clean– not full of toxic greenhouse gas emissions, and the number of patients seeking medical attention for respiratory ailments are diminished. A time when humans no longer need to think about their carbon footprint because all sources of power extracted are from renewable and ecologically friendly resources. While these expectations may seem unrealistic, they are not as far fetched as they seem. These expectations can be achieved through steps like making the switch from fossil fuel generated energy to renewable resources such as combined heat and power systems. This system can be used in conjunction with other renewable sources like gas turbines and solar powered energy. This chapter took a deep dive into the details of combined heat and power systems.

With the advantageous effects of combined heating and power systems, it is without a doubt that the system will be integrated in the typical lifestyle of future energy scenarios. Renewable energy technologies are slowly becoming implemented as energy sources and are now considered modern forms of power generation. As the population increases, the demand for energy increases as well. Many developed countries are focusing on reducing greenhouse gas emissions by increasing renewable energy usage and energy transition. One of the many renewable energy technologies include the combined heat and power system and its implementation with other forms of renewable energy systems like solar energy. Solar energy will definitely remain a major source of low cost and low emission electricity which will be considered as a key role in the next ten to thirty years for growing energy demand. As explained in the previous subchapters, the use of solar energy coupled with combined heating and power systems will definitely be beneficial for the reduction of greenhouse gas emissions and energy consumption costs.

Due to the nature of this system, it can be integrated with already commonly used sources of power like gas turbines which operate on natural gas. Combined heat and power technology can serve as an essential transition technology to a zero-carbon future. They play a vital role in a decarbonized world as they can operate on a wide variety of fuels such as biofuels and synthetic fuels like hydrogen– as discussed in this chapter. As synthetic fuels become cheaper, more industries are willing to integrate them in conjunction with combined heat and power systems. Using methods like peak and valley prices along with synthetic fuels, combined heat and power systems become a more economically strategic and environmentally friendly mode of generating energy for everyday residential consumption. This system will be the bridge that helps consumers transition to a more ecologically safe and green energy option. This change will not only help individuals flourish economically by saving money, but will help preserve the health of each other, and most importantly the only habitable planet known to humankind. There is only one planet like Earth, therefore, it must be preserved.

References

Auñón-Hidalgo, Juan Antonio, et al. "Performance and CO2 Emissions Assessment of a Novel Combined Solar Photovoltaic and Thermal, with a Stirling Engine Micro-Chp System for Domestic Environments." Energy Conversion and Management, vol. 230, 2021, p. 113793., https://doi.org/10.1016/j.enconman.2020.113793.

Bagherian, Mohammad Ali, and Kamyar Mehranzamir. "A Comprehensive Review on Renewable Energy Integration for Combined Heat and Power Production." Energy Conversion and Management, vol. 224, 2020, p. 113454., https://doi.org/10.1016/j.enconman.2020.113454.

Bagherian, Mohammad Ali, and Kamyar Mehranzamir. "A Comprehensive Review on Renewable Energy Integration for Combined Heat and Power Production." Energy Conversion and Management, vol. 224, 2020, p. 113454., https://doi.org/10.1016/j.enconman.2020.113454.

Bórawski, Piotr, et al. "Development of Renewable Energy Sources Market and Biofuels in the European Union." Journal of Cleaner Production, vol. 228, 2019, pp. 467–484., https://doi.org/10.1016/j.jclepro.2019.04.242.

"Carbon Dioxide Emissions From Electricity." World Nuclear Association, World Nuclear Association, 2020, https://www.world-nuclear.org/information-library/energy-and-the-environment/carbon-dioxide-emissions-from-electricity.aspx.

"Causes and Effects of Climate Change." Climate Action, United Nations, https://www.un.org/en/climatechange/science/causes-effects-climate-change.
"Combined Heat and Power (CHP) and District Energy." Energy.gov, U.S. Department of Energy , https://www.energy.gov/eere/amo/combined-heat-and-power-chp-and-district-energy.

"Combined Heat and Power Basics." Energy.gov, U.S. Department of Energy, https://www.energy.gov/eere/amo/combined-heat-and-power-basics.

"Combined Heat and Power Generation." GE Gas Power, General Electric, https://www.ge.com/gas-power/applications/chp.

"Combined Heat and Power." GOV.UK, Department for Business, Energy & Industrial Strategy, 22 Jan. 2013, https://www.gov.uk/guidance/combined-heat-and-power.

Dincer, Ibrahim, and Azzam Abu-Rayash. "Sustainability Modeling." Energy Sustainability, 2020, pp. 119–164., https://doi.org/10.1016/b978-0-12-819556-7.00006-1.

Gu, W, et al. "Microgrid Economic Optimal Operation of the Combined Heat and Power System with Renewable Energy." IEEE PES General Meeting, 2010, https://doi.org/10.1109/pes.2010.5590140.

Jørgensen, Sven Erik, and Yuri M. Svirezhev. "Work, Exergy and Information." Towards a Thermodynamic Theory for Ecological Systems, 2004, pp. 95–126., https://doi.org/10.1016/b978-008044166-5/50005-7.

Knowles, J. "Overview of Small and Micro Combined Heat and Power (CHP) Systems." Small and Micro Combined Heat and Power (CHP) Systems, 2011, pp. 3–16., https://doi.org/10.1533/9780857092755.1.3.

Mahian, Omid, et al. "Exergy Analysis in Combined Heat and Power Systems: A Review." Energy Conversion and Management, vol. 226, 2020, p. 113467., https://doi.org/10.1016/j.enconman.2020.113467.

Martinez, Simon, et al. "Micro-Combined Heat and Power Systems (Micro-Chp) Based on Renewable Energy Sources." Energy Conversion and Management, vol. 154, 2017, pp. 262–285., https://doi.org/10.1016/j.enconman.2017.10.035.

Chapter 7
Cities Around the World with 100% Sourced Renewable Energy

Hala Mahdi

Introduction

In a world increasingly threatened by climate change and its devastating consequences, where countries and individuals alike are realizing the importance of sustainability and acting to prevent further deterioration, the shift to renewable energy is a promising step towards positive change. Cities are a core component of these solutions, being essential for de-carbonization strategies in multiple sectors, including but not limited to energy, transport, and agriculture (European Commission 2020). Interestingly, cities account for 40% of the globe's total energy consumption and 70% of greenhouse gas emissions, while only occupying 2% of the total land ("New Urban Agenda"). The idea of cities utilizing only renewable energy to meet their demands is not a new one, and in fact significantly increasing the use of renewables has been a popular promise made by many major cities around the world in the past decade. This includes Adelaide in Australia, Amsterdam in The Netherlands, and Copenhagen in Denmark (OECD, 2020). However, only a few cities and towns have been successful in this mission thus far, and in this chapter two particular notable examples will be presented as case studies for the move to 100% sourced renewable energy for towns and cities. These examples will be Burlington, Vermont, the first U.S city to use 100% renewable sourced energy, and Reykjavik, Iceland, the capital of a country that itself completely relies on renewable energy (Herendeen 2019; Fatima et al. 2022). Specifically, the case studies will cover the current energy portfolios of these cities, how they completed the transition to renewables, and any obstacles or challenges that they faced on the way. Finally, the chapter will end with some key takeaways to keep in mind for other cities/regions wishing to make the same transition, as well as important factors to consider to maintain economic and environmental sustainability. Burlington, Vermont

Energy Supply Breakdown

Burlington's fuel source breakdown for 2021 from the most energy provided to the least is as follows: wood (136,677 MWH), wind (77,544 MWH), Large hydro (73,326 MWH), small hydro (68,620 MWH), solar (5,032 MWH), and oil (375 MWH, 0.1% of generated energy) (Burlington Energy Department 2022). This energy comes from a variety of sources, with hydro electricity coming from as far as Quebec, Canada, their wind electricity coming from 25-250 km away, and their wood energy coming from a biomass plant within 160 km (Herendeen 2019). The Burlington Electric Department's (BED) annual reports break down the provided energy thoroughly, citing that for the 2021 year their renewable resources ``provided over 100% of the total load served" by them (Burlington Energy Department 2022). Each year, they must verify that their energy portfolio is 100% renewable according to the Vermont Renewable Energy Standard through retiring Renewable Energy Credits (RECs). These RECs must be equivalent to their annual sales from generators, and they receive RECs for each MWh of renewable energy that BED generates or purchases (Burlington Energy Department 2022). This is an arduous process that must be completed to ensure validity of their claims, but is ultimately what grants Burlington the ability to proudly call itself the USA's first city with 100% renewable sourced energy (Burlington Energy Department 2022). Interestingly, although Burlington is the largest city in Vermont and is therefore the most well known for transitioning to 100% renewable sources, the trend is similar with the remainder of the state of Vermont, where renewable energy accounts for 99.5% of in-state electricity generation (U.S Energy Information Administration 2022).

The transition to renewable

The move from fossil fuels to renewable energy sources is incredibly complex, and must systematically change the region's energy supplying system. To even call something a "transition" -- as academics have been doing to this move -- is a big commitment, as it is often defined as "deep structural changes in systems, such as energy, that involve long-term and complex reconfigurations of landscapes with technology, policy, infrastructure, scientific knowledge, and social and cultural practices towards sustainable ends (Newell & Mulvaney 2013). This transition is often inequitable, and as such new terminology and concepts have been developed to push towards a more just transition, "energy justice" (Newell & Mulvaney 2013). Energy justice refers to three predominant types of justice: distributional (focusing on the origins of the injustices), recognition (examining the underrepresented and misunderstood individuals and groups), and procedural (highlighting the ways to identify and minimize the injustice) (Jenkins et al. 2015). While it is clear that this transition is a necessary one for the survival of the planet, it is also important to recognize that it is undoubtedly harmful to certain groups and individuals, and beneficial to others. In cities like Burlington where there has not been a historically high economic reliance on the fossil fuel industry, it is certainly easier to make the transition to renewable sources (Crowe & Li 2020). A just transition in other communities where many of their livelihoods are likely to be taken away as a result of the eradication of fossil fuel energy would include a focus on the creation of new jobs and ensuring economic stability outside of the fossil fuel industry (Crowe & Li 2020). A good example of this is Germany, where in the 1990s governmental programs were created following a sharp reduction in coal burning to retain the coal industry workers and help them in beginning new careers outside of the industry (Miller et al. 2013).

Residents' opinions on renewables in Burlington

With respect to Burlington, it is interesting to note that while the city and state governments are dedicated to renewable energy, there are still residents that are unhappy with the actual energy production (Crowe & Li 2020). This is specifically with regards to wind energy, where many residents in rural areas around the city are more concerned about the risks rather than the benefits. In 2014, 4 public hearings were transcribed in Burlington and 3 other Vermont municipalities (White 2014). These hearings revealed exactly this, across the state the topic of wind energy was discussed in a risk orientation nearly 350 times, while in a benefit orientation just over 50 times (White 2014). The concerns raised were varied, addressing the noise pollution created by the turbines to the power imbalance between the turbine plant developers and citizens (White 2014). Many of the concerns were related to aesthetics and wildlife, as the preferred strong wind locations in Vermont are within the state's iconically beautiful wild lands that are invaluable to state residents (Herendeen 2019). However, attitudes in Burlington generally lean against fossil fuels, regardless of any issues they may have with renewables. In another survey examining public perceptions on coal and solar energy, as well as support for energy transition policies, residents of Burlington are less likely than residents of Saline County Illinois and Houston, Texas (the other two U.S locations surveyed) to have a positive attitude towards coal (Crowe & Li 2020). The study's authors attribute this to Burlington's lack of historical economic ties to the coal and fossil fuel industry, again highlighting the importance of ensuring a just transition considerate of the circumstances of different communities with regards to fossil fuels and renewables (Crowe & Li 2020).

Defining renewability; An Ongoing Conflict

The definition of renewability, while apparently clear at first, is not as simple as it seems. It is a complicated and increasingly political definition, and one that is especially prone to change over time. Vermont is a prime example of this, where small hydroelectric generators have always been declared renewable in the state, but large hydro generators (> 200MW) did not meet the renewable criteria for two decades until 2010 when this decision was reversed through legislature (Herendeen 2019). As mentioned prior, large hydro is a massive portion of Burlington's energy portfolio, and it certainly would not meet the 100% renewable threshold if it wasn't considered a renewable source. This is a common occurrence in many other U.S states, where hydropower is a contested energy source in terms of renewability. While it is clean energy that emits minimal greenhouse gasses and cannot be depleted, it is not entirely environmentally sustainable. The land flooding required for building hydroelectric reservoirs has massive environmental impacts, destroying wildlife habitats, agricultural lands, and forests alike ("Environmental Impacts of Hydroelectric Power"). This directly goes against the definition of sustainability provided by the U.S's own environmental protection agency, "creating and maintaining conditions under which humans and nature can exist in productive harmony to support present and future generations" (US EPA 2022).

The Future: Burlington's Desire for Locally Sourced Energy vs The Spatial Impact of Renewable Energy

The BED's 2030 goal is to make Burlington a "net zero energy city" across electric, ground transportation and thermal sectors by expanding local renewable generation (Burlington Energy Department 2022). A problem with expanding local generation is the massive amounts of land that are required for the task. This is a common area of concern for renewable energy courses, with a clear example being the province of Quebec, where one fifth of its total area is covered by hydroelectricity plants (Herendeen 2019). Bringing it back to Burlington, according to several estimates, if biomass (wood, in this case) generated in Burlington were to be solely used to power the city, 3030% of Burlington's area would be needed (Herendeen 2019). If Burlington wanted to produce its current electric energy demands from wind, it would require using 43% of the city's area, which is impossible as the city is: (a) not at a high enough altitude for strong winds, and (b) this area is occupied and already in use (Herendeen 2019). These are just two examples using sources that are widely used in the city, but demonstrate the low probability that the city would actually be able to completely source its energy locally while remaining 100% renewable. If extrapolated to the state level, similar issues arise, where according to current energy usage and land use data, it is impossible for Vermont to achieve a 100% renewably sourced energy portfolio while also keeping all the generation within its borders (Herendeen 2019).

Another Perspective: Reykjavik, Iceland

Reykjavik is a unique case, and so is its country Iceland. Almost 100% of the energy consumed by Iceland is sourced renewable, with 9 out of 10 homes being specifically powered by geothermal energy (Logadóttir 2015). Iceland's natural geography lends itself almost perfectly for renewable energy sourcing, with the country lying between North American and Eurasian tectonic plates on an active volcanic zone (Logadóttir 2015). This is what largely powers the island's geothermal systems. Further, its glacial rivers powering the country's hydropower resources are maintained by the seasonal melting of the glaciers that cover ~11% of the island (Logadóttir 2015). These two geographical features alone are enough to allow the country to run almost solely on renewable energy, with the exception of their transportation being powered by fossil fuels. Reykjavik, the capital city of Iceland and in fact the northernmost capital city in the world, also sources all of its electricity and heat from renewable sources (Fatima et al. 2022). The breakdown for this in the city is 71% from hydropower sources, and 29% from geothermal sources, specifically with 80% of homes running on geothermal energy (Fatima et al. 2022).

Iceland's transition from fossil fuels to renewables

Iceland began its transition in the 1960s, only two decades after gaining independence in 1944 (Michelson 2022). It starts with, as mentioned prior, a geographical predisposition to renewables. From an engineering standpoint, it is widely recognized that the country's terrain, climate, and hydrological conditions provide countless opportunities for not only hydroelectricity, but also wind energy, a recently budding prospect (Benediktsson 2021). This is not even taking into account the abundant geothermal fields on the island, ranging from high temperature fields in the volcanically active zones to the widely scattered low temperature fields (Benediktsson 2021).

At the start of the 20th century when the island was mostly rural, reliance was largely on traditional energy sources, but with urbanization occurring as the century progressed, energy demand was higher than ever (Benediktsson 2021). Interestingly, during and before the 1960s, imported fossil fuels seemed to be promising as the major fuel source, but soon after it would be clear that hydroelectricity and geothermal energy trumped them out (Benediktsson 2021). The graph below (Fig 1.0) depicts this transition by showing the primary sources of energy used in Iceland from the 1940s to 2019. As aforementioned, the big transition occurred in the 1960s, partly due to the first large hydropower station being built on one of the island's glacial rivers (Logadóttir 2015). After that, development of other large-scale hydropower stations occurred throughout the country, with the largest dam being the Kárahnjúkar dam having a capacity of 690 MW and commissioned in 2007 (Benediktsson 2021). Geothermal energy has a slightly different past, geothermal water being traditionally used for bathing then becoming increasingly utilized for indoor heating in the 20th century, and finally currently having the vast majority of Icelandic homes fully relying on geothermal energy (Benediktsson 2021).

The energy portfolio of the country since the 1940s is shown in Figure 2.0, where we can see the transition from coal in the 1940s, to oil until the 1960s, then hydropower and geothermal after that point (Benediktsson 2021). Currently, the biggest sectors still dependent on oil energy are shipping, fishing, aviation, and land transportation (Benediktsson 2021).

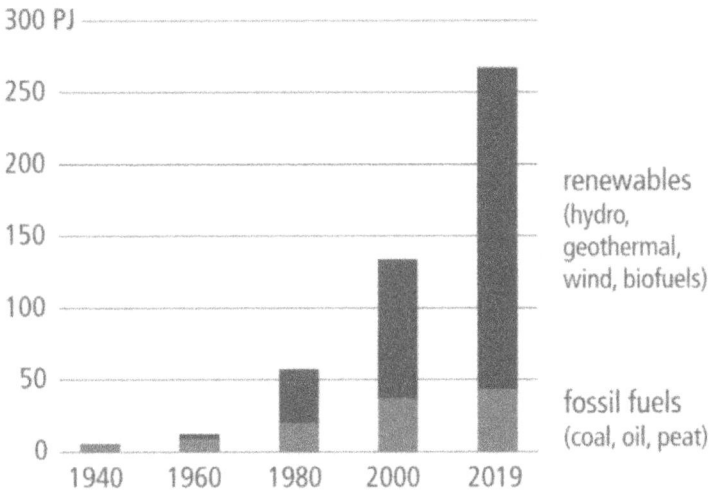

Fig 1.0: Primary sources of energy (in petajoules) in Iceland since 1940 (Benediktsson 2021)

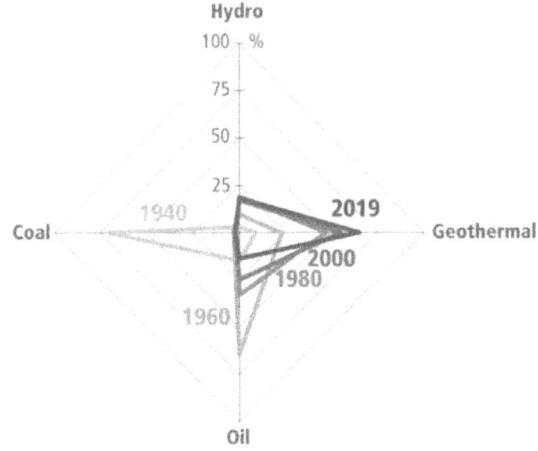

Fig 2.0: The evolving Icelandic energy portfolio from 1940 to 2019 (Benediktsson 2021)

A closer look at the transition - from local to national

Something to note is that in the 1960s and 1970s, when the majority of Iceland's transition occurred, it was not due to climate change that this decision was made (Logadóttir 2015). Instead, it was largely due to increasing prices of imported oil and Iceland's incapability of sustaining these fluctuations (Logadóttir 2015). Its location being so close to the Arctic Circle meant that any imported energy was bound to be expensive, not even accounting for market fluctuations, so there was a demand for economically sustainable domestic energy sourcing (Logadóttir 2015). The story for this change is quite inspirational too, beginning with local entrepreneurs rather than big fancy government projects (Michelson 2022).

In the early 1900s, one Icelandic farmer developed an early geothermal heating system for his farm simply using hot water coming out of the ground (Michelson 2022) . Word got around to municipalities nearby and eventually across the country, leading to a systematic approach to this new energy source (Logadóttir 2015). Interestingly, it was the drilling technology initially used by the oil industry that promoted the large-scale use of geothermal power to heat homes by allowing deeper drilling of hotter water (Logadóttir 2015). Even hydropower was once a farmer-led project; prior to the large-scale hydropower stations previously mentioned, it was dedicated farmers who developed early hydro projects as a cooperative effort to power their farms with electricity (Logadóttir 2015). Not only did the government not push these developments in the early 20th century, but in fact they hindered the potential rapid growth of the hydroelectricity industry. In the earlier decades of the 1900s, Icelandic politicians opposed entrepreneurial ideas of allowing European investors to essentially buy Icelandic waterfalls to build hydropower stations on ("The Hydro and Geothermal History"). This delayed the utilization of the island's natural resource for decades despite the potential ideas of large dams and stations pushed forth by locals ("The Hydro and Geothermal History"). As a result, only small, farmer-led hydropower projects could be built, but they still impressively increased in number throughout the first half of the century, resulting in 530 of such independent stations having been built in the country by 1950(Logadóttir 2015). In the late 1960s is when the government became more active in the renewable energy space. They established a geothermal drilling mitigation fund that loaned money for new geothermal research and provided cost recovery for failed projects (Logadóttir 2015). This, predictably, increased interest in geothermal prospects and incentivised individuals and businesses alike to move away from fossil fuels.

Conclusion:
The lessons learned from Burlington and Reykjavik

The two cases presented in this chapter are certainly from two very different countries with different terrains, climates, politics, economies, you name it. However, there are a few key takeaways from their respective journeys to renewable energy that can be applied as common frameworks for other cities wishing to do the same. First, we can see from both of those examples that the journey to renewable began small, in local municipalities, smaller cities, and continued growing to reach a larger scale (whether this be state-wide in the case of Burlington or nation-wide with Reykjavik). Municipal governments have shown to have immense influence and power for the energy transition, and can continue to inspire and influence other municipalities around them. Additionally, it is crucial to ensure that both the public, businesses, and the lawmakers are on the same page. It is also important to keep in mind that an economy and public who are reliant on fossil fuels for their livelihoods are not likely to support a transition to renewable energy that does not provide them with the same opportunities. Therefore, the government needs to get involved in providing funds, bursaries, and job opportunities to ensure a sustainable and scalable transition.

Another aspect to keep in mind is to remain positive and showcase individual successes to motivate the public and keep morale up. The transition is a difficult one that requires decades of hard work and dedication from everyone involved. This includes the consumers of the energy. To garner the support of the public who will ultimately vote for the lawmakers, give business to the companies, and consume the energy, they must be convinced that progress is being made and it is for the greater good of everyone. This was exemplified well in Iceland, where municipalities that found success in transitioning to geothermal energy became role models for others around them. "Before and after" photos were used by politicians to attract voter attention to the results of the geothermal energy transition through cleaner air and lower costs compared to fossil fuels (Logadóttir 2015).

In the end however, it is important to recognize that not every city will realistically be able to make this transition in the near future. There are certain regions that are incredibly heavily reliant on fossil fuels, with entire communities' livelihood and economic stability depending on the industry. Additionally, not every city/state/region/country will have the natural resources and geographical features to locally source renewable energy, which complicates the transition as it will undoubtedly cost more to switch to renewables in that case. Further, it is also crucial to consider environmental ramifications of renewable energy, including noise pollution from wind turbines, and major land occupation and ecosystem destruction by massive hydro plants, to name a few examples. While these are not reasons to never consider transitioning to renewable energy, they are all very valid factors in the decision making leading up to it, and that must be mitigated prior to starting the process. It is only once these factors are accounted for that an economically and environmentally sustainable transition to renewable energy will be made.

References

Benediktsson, Karl. "Conflicting Imaginaries in the Energy Transition? Nature and Renewable Energy in Iceland." Moravian Geographical Reports, vol. 29, no. 2, June 2021, pp. 88–100. DOI.org (Crossref), https://doi.org/10.2478/mgr-2021-0008.

Crowe, Jessica A., and Ruopu Li. "Is the Just Transition Socially Accepted? Energy History, Place, and Support for Coal and Solar in Illinois, Texas, and Vermont." Energy Research & Social Science, vol. 59, Jan. 2020, p. 101309. DOI.org (Crossref), https://doi.org/10.1016/j.erss.2019.101309.

Environmental Impacts of Hydroelectric Power | Union of Concerned Scientists. https://www.ucsusa.org/resources/environmental-impacts-hydroelectric-power.

European Commission Directorate-General for. 100 Climate-Neutral Cities by 2030 - by and for the Citizens: Interim Report of the Mission Board for Climate-Neutral and Smart Cities. Publications Office of the European Union, 2020, https://books.google.ca/books?id=k3LHzQEACAAJ.

Fatima, Zarrin, et al. "Getting Started with Positive Energy Districts: Experience until Now from Maia, Reykjavik, Kifissia, Kladno and Lviv." Sustainability, vol. 14, no. 10, May 2022, p. 5799. DOI.org (Crossref), https://doi.org/10.3390/su14105799.

Herendeen, Robert. "Does '100% Renewable' Trump Concern for Spatial Impacts?" Energy Policy, vol. 130, July 2019, pp. 304–10. DOI.org (Crossref), https://doi.org/10.1016/j.enpol.2019.04.002.

Jenkins, Kirsten, et al. "Energy Justice: A Conceptual Review." Energy Research & Social Science, vol. 11, Jan. 2016, pp. 174–82. DOI.org (Crossref), https://doi.org/10.1016/j.erss.2015.10.004.

(Logadóttir 2015), Halla Hrund. "Iceland's Sustainable Energy Story: A Model for the World?" United Nations, United Nations, Dec. 2015, https://www.un.org/en/chronicle/article/icelands-sustainable-energy-story-model-world.

Michelson, Joan. "7 Renewable Energy Strategies We Can Learn From Iceland." Forbes, 28 June 2022, https://www.forbes.com/sites/joanmichelson2/2022/06/28/iceland-runs-on-85-renewable-energy-7-strategies-we-can-learn-from-them/.

Miller, Clark A., et al. "The Social Dimensions of Energy Transitions." Science as Culture, vol. 22, no. 2, June 2013, pp. 135–48. DOI.org (Crossref), https://doi.org/10.1080/09505431.2013.786989.
New Urban Agenda: H III: Habitat III: Quito 17-20 October 2016. United Nations, 2017.

Newell, Peter, and Dustin Mulvaney. "The Political Economy of the 'Just Transition': The Political Economy of the 'Just Transition.'" The Geographical

Journal, vol. 179, no. 2, June 2013, pp. 132–40. DOI.org (Crossref), https://doi.org/10.1111/geoj.12008.

OECD. Managing Environmental and Energy Transitions for Regions and Cities. OECD, 2020. DOI.org (Crossref), https://doi.org/10.1787/f0c6621f-en. Our Energy Portfolio – Burlington Electric Department. https://www.burlingtonelectric.com/our-energy-portfolio. Accessed 29 Jan. 2023.

"The Hydro and Geothermal History." Askja Energy - The Essential Perspective on Energy in the Northern Atlantic and Arctic Region, 11 Nov. 2011, https://askjaenergy.com/iceland-renewable-energy-sources/hydro-and-geothermal-history/.

U.S. Energy Information Administration - EIA - Independent Statistics and Analysis. https://www.eia.gov/state/?sid=VT.

US EPA, OP. Learn About Sustainability. 5 Nov. 2014, https://www.epa.gov/sustainability/learn-about-sustainability.

White, Joanna Elizabeth, "Renewable Energy Zoning: Cutting Green Tape While Improving Ecological Outcomes for Renewable Energy Projects" (2014). Graduate College Dissertations and Theses. 284.https://scholarworks.uvm.edu/graddis/284

Chapter 8
Decentralized Wind Power

Michael Phan

What is Decentralized Wind Power

A shift away from a centralized power grid, wherein power is generated by a number of major power plants and dispersed over distant locations, is commonly known as decentralization in the energy industry (Jin 2018). Alternatively, a model where energy is both produced and sourced in local neighborhoods is proposed. This concept boosts the use of renewable energy sources, decreases dependency on huge, centralized power plants, and improves the overall efficiency of energy and its subsidiaries (Jin 2018). Communities are able to have greater control over their energy production and use while also being able to improve their resilience to power outages by moving away from a centralized system (Jin 2018).

Decentralized wind power is a renewable energy system that is dispersed over many areas. This sort of technology enables a more effective use of renewable energy by generating wind power closer to the people who need it rather than depending on massive centralized wind farms (Morthorst 2003). This method also contributes to lowering the environmental effect of wind energy by allowing turbines to be installed in more remote areas with less noise and visual impact (Morthorst 2003). Furthermore, decentralized wind power can assist in cutting energy costs since it is more cost-effective to construct and maintain wind turbines in several places rather than in a centralized wind farm. Decentralized wind generation can also assist to improve energy supply dependability since the turbines can be dispersed across a larger region and are less impacted by changing weather conditions (Morthorst 2003). Countries and communities may profit from a clean and dependable renewable energy source by employing decentralized wind power.

Decentralized wind power has some advantages over solar power and hydropower. Firstly, wind power is more accessible and can be produced in many different locations, meaning it is easier to install and maintain. Secondly, wind turbines require less initial investment compared to solar power and hydropower. Thirdly, wind power is not as dependent on weather conditions as solar power, and is less expensive than hydropower. Lastly, wind turbines produce clean energy without producing any emissions.

However, decentralized wind power has some drawbacks compared to solar power and hydropower. Firstly, the energy produced by wind turbines is intermittent and unpredictable, making it difficult to use for grid-level power supply. Secondly, wind turbines are noisy and can be intrusive in certain areas. Additionally, wind turbines can be difficult to maintain and require a lot of space. Lastly, wind turbines can be hazardous to animals, such as birds, due to their spinning blades.

History of decentralized wind power

The rise of wind power
Wind power is a form of renewable energy that harnesses the energy of the wind to generate electricity. It has been used for centuries for a variety of purposes, such as grinding grain, pumping water, and providing mechanical power for sailing ships. The modern age of wind power began in the late 19th century when the first wind turbine was built in Scotland (Cabinet Secretary for Rural Affairs and Islands, n.d.). Since then, wind power has grown rapidly and is now a major

contributor to the global energy supply. The rise of wind power has been driven by advances in technology, as well as by increasing public awareness of the need for renewable energy sources (Johansen 2021). Governments have also played a role in promoting wind power through various incentive programs (Johansen 2021). As technology continues to improve and the cost of wind energy continues to decrease, the use of wind power is likely to continue to grow in the coming years.

Wind power's development into a decentralized system
Wind power's development into a decentralized system is the result of technological advances in the wind energy industry (Office of Energy Efficiency & Renewable Energy 2022). It allows for the installation of small, local wind turbines as opposed to larger, centralized wind farms. This decentralization of wind energy allows for more efficient use of resources, cost savings, and increased reliability. The decentralized system also makes it easier for individuals and businesses to access wind energy, as the cost to install a local wind turbine is much lower than the cost to install a large wind farm (Office of Energy Efficiency & Renewable Energy 2022b). Additionally, the decentralized system enables more efficient distribution of power, as the electricity generated from small wind turbines can be used locally and not need to be transported over long distances (Office of Energy Efficiency & Renewable Energy 2022b). This reduces the amount of energy lost during transmission and increases the amount of renewable energy available.

How decentralized wind power works

Generators and turbines
Decentralized wind power works by leveraging small turbines and generators to capture and convert the wind's kinetic energy into usable electricity. Typically, these turbines are either mounted on the ground

or on rooftops, and they capture the energy of the wind and convert it into electricity (Desalegn, Gebeyehu, and Tamirat 2022). This electricity can then be used to power a variety of applications, such as lighting, heating, cooling, and more. Additionally, some systems may also allow users to sell the excess energy they generate back to the grid, providing a potential source of income for the user (Desalegn, Gebeyehu, and Tamirat 2022).

To further aid in the decision-making process, it is important to consider the overall cost of the system, the size of the generator, the available wind speeds in the area, the specific energy needs of the home, and the amount of maintenance required to keep the system running efficiently. Additionally, it is important to research the warranties that are offered with the generator, as well as the installation costs, to ensure that the product is reliable and cost-effective. By thoroughly researching the various types of wind-powered generators, homeowners can make a confident and informed decision that is best for their individual needs.

Vertical Axis Wind Turbines (VAWT) are a form of wind turbine that rests on a vertical axis rather than the typical horizontal axis. This sort of turbine is frequently used in small-scale applications like powering a home or a small company. The advantages are that they are more efficient at lower wind speeds, can be put on roofs, and require less maintenance than standard horizontal axis turbines. Cons: They are often more costly than standard turbines, and the blades are more susceptible to damage from severe winds (Moreno-Armendáriz et al. 2021).

Micro wind turbines are relatively small wind turbines that are often installed on building roofs of buildings or even other structures. These turbines may greatly supplement standard energy sources like electricity. They are generally affordable, simple to deploy, and may be put in tight spaces. However, they are usually less efficient than bigger wind turbines and can only produce a limited quantity of electricity.

Buoy mounted wind turbines are a kind of ocean-based floating wind turbine. These turbines take advantage of the regular winds that are prevalent in the ocean and may generate a substantial amount of electrical energy (Knopper et al. 2014). They are less costly than standard turbines and may be installed in distant regions with high winds. Cons: They are challenging to install in deep water and require a lot of maintenance.

Solar-wind hybrid systems will typically in a sense combine the power of solar panels with the power of wind turbines. This sort of device is frequently employed in remote locations when traditional energy sources are scarce or even limited and inadequate. They are relatively efficient and can create a significant quantity of energy (Knopper et al. 2014). Cons: They are difficult to maintain and can be cost a significant amount of money to install.

Connecting decentralized wind power to the grid
Connecting decentralized wind power to the grid is a major part of the effort to create an energy infrastructure that is more sustainable and reliable. Wind power produces electricity without the need for traditional fossil fuel sources, making it a clean and renewable source of energy for many countries (Knopper et al. 2014). By connecting decentralized wind power sources to the grid, electricity can be generated and distributed to customers, reducing our reliance on fossil fuels and providing clean energy to consumers. The process of connecting decentralized wind power to the grid is complex and involves several components. First, the wind turbine must be connected to the local grid (Moreno-Armendáriz et al. 2021). This involves running underground wires from the turbine

to the nearest grid substation. The connection must be made in a way that ensures the safety of both the turbine and the grid.

Once the turbine is connected to the grid, it must be registered with the local energy provider. This allows the energy provider to track energy production and ensure that the turbine is producing enough energy to meet the needs of consumers. The local energy provider will also work to optimize the connection, helping to reduce the amount of energy lost in transmission. The next step is to ensure that the decentralized wind power is integrated into the grid (Moreno-Armendáriz et al. 2021). This involves connecting the turbine to the grid network, which is usually done through a control system. This allows the energy provider to monitor the turbine and make sure that it is producing the correct amount of energy (Moreno-Armendáriz et al. 2021). Finally, the energy provider must ensure that the energy produced by the turbine is distributed to customers in an efficient manner. This involves using smart meters and other technologies to ensure that the energy is sent to the right place at the right time.

Connecting decentralized wind power to the grid is a complex process, but it is essential if we want to create a more sustainable and reliable energy infrastructure. By connecting decentralized wind power sources to the grid, electricity can be generated and distributed to customers, reducing our reliance on fossil fuels and providing clean energy to consumers.

Advantages of decentralized wind power
Decentralized wind power is a growing renewable energy source that provides several benefits to people, organizations, and communities. The public may have access to clean, renewable energy in a more cost-effective and dependable manner than traditional power sources by utilizing decentralized wind turbines. Decentralized wind generation has

the ability to lower energy costs, create jobs, and promote community energy independence. It is also a less harmful alternative to fossil fuels that can help reduce carbon emissions. Decentralized wind power is an appealing choice for individuals wishing to invest in renewable energy due to its numerous benefits (Strandberg 2021).

Cost savings

Cost savings: Furthermore, decentralized wind systems can help reduce the amount of energy lost in transmission. Because they are located closer to where the electricity is used, fewer losses are incurred during the delivery process. This can improve the efficiency of the electricity grid, which helps lower electricity costs overall (Strandberg 2021). Additionally, decentralized systems are often located in more remote areas, which means they can produce energy in places where large-scale wind farms may not be feasible. This can open up new opportunities for communities to access renewable energy, and help them become more self-sufficient.

Reduced carbon footprint

Decentralized wind power reduces carbon footprints by harnessing the power of the wind to generate electricity without relying on traditional fossil fuel-based power plants. This eliminates the need to burn fossil fuels, which produces high levels of emissions. Additionally, wind is a renewable energy source, meaning it can provide a consistent, clean source of energy without the need to replenish it. This further reduces the carbon footprint of the energy source (Strandberg 2021).

Increased reliability

Decentralized wind power has become more reliable over time as technology advances and new techniques are developed. For instance, better turbine designs, improved maintenance techniques, and better forecasting and control systems have all contributed to more reliable wind power (Strandberg 2021). Additionally, the use of energy storage systems to store excess wind energy for later use has allowed wind power to become more reliable. Finally, the deployment of smart grid systems, which are able to efficiently manage and distribute electricity from multiple sources, has also enhanced the reliability of decentralized wind power.

Reduced Transmission Losses

Electricity can sometimes get lost in long-distance transmission lines due to resistance in the lines. As electricity passes through the transmission lines, some of it is converted to heat and is lost as energy. Additionally, when electricity is transmitted over long distances, it is necessary to step up the voltage to reduce the amount of current flowing through the lines, which can also lead to some energy loss (Strandberg 2021). Finally, when electricity is transmitted over long distances, it is prone to electromagnetic induction, which can cause energy to be lost from the lines. Decentralized wind power can thus help to reduce the need for long-distance transmission lines altogether, which can be expensive to construct and maintain. This means that more of the electricity generated can be used to benefit the local community, rather than being lost in transmission (Strandberg 2021). Additionally, decentralized wind power can be beneficial for those areas that are far away from the main electricity grid, as it can provide a more reliable and cost-effective source of energy. Furthermore, it can provide increased energy security, as it is not dependent on any one energy source. Finally, it can also help to reduce carbon emissions, as it does not require burning fossil fuels to generate electricity (Strandberg 2021).

Increased energy security

Decentralized wind power systems are less susceptible to interruption or sabotage than larger, centralized systems, increasing energy security. This gives communities a greater level of control over their energy supply, as well as the ability to respond quickly and effectively to any disruptions (Strandberg 2021).

Lower environmental impact
Decentralized wind power systems emit no pollutants into the air or water and have a far lower environmental effect than traditional kinds of energy generating. This can help to reduce the strain on the environment, as well as help to preserve natural resources (Strandberg 2021).

Low noise pollution
Decentralized wind turbines are much quieter than traditional energy sources, reducing noise pollution in the surrounding area and helping to improve the quality of life for those living close to the turbines. This is especially beneficial for those living in rural areas, where sound pollution from traditional energy sources such as coal and gas plants can be particularly disruptive. Wind turbines are also more efficient than other energy sources, meaning that less power is needed to achieve the same result. Furthermore, wind turbines produce fewer emissions, helping to reduce air pollution and the associated health risks. These advantages of wind energy make it an ideal alternative to traditional energy sources, resulting in a cleaner, quieter environment.

Local job creation
Decentralized wind power systems generate local jobs in the turbine production, installation, and maintenance, as well as extra job prospects in the communities where the turbines are installed. This can help to create sustainable employment opportunities in rural or remote areas, providing much needed economic benefits to the local community. (Office of Energy Efficiency & Renewable Energy 2022).

Disadvantages of decentralized wind power

1. High Upfront Cost:

When compared to traditional energy sources such as coal or natural gas, decentralized wind power systems can be costly. Purchase, maintenance, and operation of wind turbines and associated equipment may very well break the bank. Furthermore, the construction of decentralized wind power systems, particularly in remote places, sometimes necessitates significant investment in transmission infrastructure, which can add to the overall cost. Government incentives and subsidies can be used to decrease the initial cost of installation, and economies of scale can be used to minimize the cost of acquiring and maintaining the turbines.

2. Weather Dependence:

Wind power can very often be unreliable and susceptible to weather and climatic fluctuations. It goes without saying that the turbines cannot generate power when the wind is not blowing. This makes relying on dispersed wind power as a major energy source challenging. Other renewable energy sources, such as solar or hydro power, might be included into the system, as well as improved energy storage technologies to store energy created while the wind is blowing for use when it is not.

3. Environmental Effect:

Wind turbines may have a major environmental impact, including animal disturbance, and visual pollution. Often, wind turbines can be deadly to birds, especially those that migrate through wind turbine zones. Solutions include using radar technology to detect the presence of birds and installing bird deterrent devices such as lights and sound systems. Furthermore, careful design of wind turbine placement might assist to limit the danger of bird death. Use of turbines particularly built to reduce their environmental impact, such as quieter turbines or those designed to prevent disturbing bird migration patterns, is one solution to this problem. Moreover, the location of the turbines should be carefully considered in order to limit their influence on nearby flora and animals.

4. Noise Pollution:
Due to the continual rotating of the blades, wind turbines can produce noise pollution. This can be upsetting for residents who live near the turbines and have a detrimental influence on their quality of life. Solutions include using quieter designs and installing noise-reducing barriers or screens. Wind turbines may also be constructed to function more efficiently, which can assist to lessen the noise they emit.

5. Land Use:
In order to be effective and efficient, wind turbines require a considerable area of land. This can be an issue in locations where land is rare or expensive, making decentralized wind generating plants difficult to build and run. Solutions include developing small-scale wind turbines that are more efficient and use less land, as well as using floating turbines that can be deployed offshore.

Conclusion

Decentralized wind power is an exciting and successful form of renewable energy. Its many benefits include reducing dependence on fossil fuels, cost savings, increased energy security, lower environmental impact, low noise pollution, increased reliability, reduced transmission losses, and local job creation. This makes decentralized wind power a great option for those looking to transition to renewable energy sources. It is important to research and understand which decentralized wind power generator will suit your needs the most. Decentralized wind power is a great way to ensure that our energy needs are met in a sustainable and efficient manner. With these benefits in mind, it is clear to see why decentralized wind power is an attractive option for those looking to transition to renewable energy sources.

References

Cabinet Secretary for Rural Affairs and Islands. n.d. "Offshore Wind Energy." Www.gov.scot. https://www.gov.scot/policies/marine-renewable-energy/offshore-wind-energy/#:~:text=Scotland%20is%20home%20to%20the.

Desalegn, Belachew, Desta Gebeyehu, and Bimrew Tamirat. 2022. "Wind Energy Conversion Technologies and Engineering Approaches to Enhancing Wind Power Generation: A Review." Heliyon 8 (11): e11263. https://doi.org/10.1016/j.heliyon.2022.e11263.

Jin, Sang-Hyeon. 2018. "The Definition and Direction of Energy Autonomy: Focusing on Decentralization." The Korean Journal of Local Government Studies 22 (3): 31–58. https://doi.org/10.20484/klog.22.3.2.
Johansen, Katinka. 2021. "Blowing in the Wind: A Brief History of Wind Energy and Wind Power Technologies in Denmark." Energy Policy, March, 112139. https://doi.org/10.1016/j.enpol.2021.112139.

Knopper, Loren D., Christopher A. Ollson, Lindsay C. McCallum, Melissa L. Whitfield Aslund, Robert G. Berger, Kathleen Souweine, and Mary McDaniel. 2014. "Wind Turbines and Human Health." Frontiers in Public Health 2 (June). https://doi.org/10.3389/fpubh.2014.00063.

Moreno-Armendáriz, Marco A., Carlos A. Duchanoy, Hiram Calvo, Eddy Ibarra-Ontiveros, Jesua S. Salcedo-Castañeda, Michel Ayala-Canseco, and Damián García. 2021. "Wind Booster Optimization for On-Site Energy Generation Using Vertical-Axis Wind Turbines." Sensors 21 (14): 4775. https://doi.org/10.3390/s21144775.

Morthorst, P. E. 2003. "Wind Power and the Conditions at a Liberalized Power Market." Wind Energy 6 (3): 297–308. https://doi.org/10.1002/we.92.

Office of Energy Efficiency & Renewable Energy. 2022a. "Advantages and Challenges of Wind Energy." Energy.gov. Office of Energy Efficiency & Renewable Energy. 2022. https://www.energy.gov/eere/wind/advantages-and-challenges-wind-energy.

———. 2022b. "Distributed Wind." Energy.gov. 2022. https://www.energy.gov/eere/wind/distributed-wind.

Strandberg, Li. 2021. "Decentralized Energy Systems Give Advantages." Www.iiiee.lu.se. Lund University. February 17, 2021. https://www.iiiee.lu.se/article/decentralized-energy-systems-give-advantages.

Chapter 9
Decentralized Solar Power

Freddie Montague

What is solar energy?
Solar radiation (or light) emitted by the sun is a form of electromagnetic radiation. Solar panels capture and convert electromagnetic radiation into usable forms of energy (Zweibel, 2013). Solar energy can be harnessed directly or indirectly for human use and involves the use of photovoltaic (PV) panels or mirrors to concentrate solar radiation and convert it into electricity to be used for heating, cooling, and light. Solar energy is recognized as a renewable or "green" power source, and is an alternative to traditional energy production, like the burning of fossil fuels. Solar energy is part of our clean energy future. The energy that is generated from solar panels can be stored in batteries or thermal storage ("How Does Solar Work?").

Solar power was first discovered by French physicist Edmond Becquerel in 1839. This young scientist (being only 19 years old at the time) observed the photovoltaic effect when experimenting in his father's lab. This was the process that turns sunlight into electricity. He did this by placing two plates made of either gold or platinum in a conducting solution, followed by their exposure to solar radiation. This photovoltaic effect he observed is also referred to as the Becquerel effect. ("Solar Power Guide") As the following decades went on, more and more scientists expanded on this discovery, eventually giving us the solar power system that we know and use today.

How does centralized solar energy work vs. decentralized solar energy? Centralized solar energy operates via large-scale plant installations, usually in remote areas. The solar electricity produced is abundant and fed into a grid, often reaching recipients far away via transmission lines for their use (Gupta, 2014). Solar energy could be a solution to the lack of access to electricity in many parts of the world. 20% of the world population lacks access to modern forms of energy like solar, and 13% has no access to electricity at all, a total of 940 million people (Ritchie et al., 2022). Since access to energy is linked to human well-being, it is a priority to bring energy to the developing world. Additionally, from an efficiency perspective in North America, it is also a priority to improve the systems already in place. For these reasons and more, decentralized solar power may be the way to go.

Decentralized solar power operates at a technical level in the same way that centralized solar power operates; with the goal of turning solar energy into electricity and solar thermal energy. However, with decentralized solar energy, the solar panels are installed on buildings' rooftops for direct use, or are located in other places that are not centrally located. (Gupta, 2014) Decentralized energy is produced off the main grid and alternatively is produced close to where it will be used. Ohiare (2013) states that "the aim of the technology is to integrate within a distributed generation framework to provide rural areas of developing countries with a micro-grid platform that can be manufactured and assembled locally (unlike PV collectors) and can replace or supplement Diesel generators in off grid areas, by generating clean power at a lower levelized cost." Decentralized solar energy can be on the household/business level (stand-alone) or on the community level (micro-grid); meaning that individuals can possess their own personal solar panels and generate their own electricity to be used by them alone. Differently, decentralized solar power can be systems of interconnected buildings that combine multiple energy carriers (electricity, heat) and are able to store the renewable energy.

Why decentralized solar energy is better than centralized solar energy (pros)

There are many problems with the centralized solar power network that can be solved with decentralization. The following highlights the advantages to decentralized power systems in general compared to centralized power systems that can be applied to the solar power industry.

More energy efficient: To begin, centralized solar energy is not efficient for spread out populations. When the energy is produced at one central location, it must travel long distances in order to be consumed, meaning that voltage and efficiency is lost over time (Gupta, 2014). It is estimated that 30-60% of electricity is lost with this energy delivery method (Gupta, 2014). This problem is minimized with decentralized solar energy, as the energy is produced on-site or nearby meaning that there is less loss of voltage and efficiency.

More space efficient: Another issue encountered with centralized solar energy production is the requirement for the development of large plots of land (Gupta, 2014). With decentralized solar energy production, unused rooftop space can be used to house the solar panels. This also has economic benefits, as the development of land for centralized solar power plants is expensive. Buildings with a lot of unused roof space would be good candidates for a decentralized solar power system, like schools and office buildings.

More resilient to power grid breakdowns: Central solar power is also more resilient to electricity grid breakdowns. With central plants, one issue with the grid can affect millions of people, as businesses, essential services, and households are connected to the same grid. For instance, this was an issue that occurred in northern India in 2001, when almost all of the region was in a blackout due to the breakdown of just one substation that affected the entire grid (Gupta, 2014). This had an immense impact on the economy, as 107.1 million dollars were lost due to this incident. As stated by Gupta (2014), "There will be no single points of failure that can bring down the whole grid, as there is with centralized power generation. The impact of intentionally created disasters, will also be minimized".

Increased grid flexibility: A decentralized energy system increases energy resilience, which is an important trait to have, especially with unpredictable political climates, like the one caused by the war in Ukraine, for example. Decentralized energy systems allow markets to adapt to changing conditions readily and recover quickly from any issues or disruptions. Decentralized power systems will also be beneficial for when centralized grid failures occur due to weather ("Can Decentralized Energy Get Good Enough Fast Enough?").
More employment friendly: The decentralization of solar power can provide new job opportunities, as personal solar panels will become a common

household appliance. Technicians and mechanics will be needed to assess and resolve any issues with the system, and small businesses will likely pop up to provide and organize these services and provide maintenance (Gupta, 2014). More government efficient: With distributed solar energy production, it is less likely that the government will get involved. This is because decentralizing energy systems in general will move decision making from the top administrator of a branch of government to lower-level officials (Gupta, 2014). More cost efficient: With centralized solar power systems, certain materials are required for operation that are not needed for decentralized solar power systems, such as long transmission lines and large transformer stations (Gupta, 2014). This in combination to the monetary losses caused by voltage loss, our current solar power system is not the most cost efficient. With decentralized solar power systems, money is saved as these issues are not encountered. From a personal perspective, customers can also save money by selling unused energy that they collect back to power companies, giving them a little extra money in their pockets. Solar panels last for 25-30 years on average (Church, 2022), and so overtime, the high up-front investment made will likely pay for itself, as one is no longer paying monthly for electricity and is instead generating free solar electricity from the sun with no effort. Additionally, with a centralized system, it is very expensive to expand into rural communities that have a low population density, as the power will not serve many people ("Planning Energy Access: Centralized or Decentralized Electrification"). Help reduce greenhouse gasses: Renewable energy sources in general are environmentally friendly alternatives to the burning of non-renewable fossil fuels. The potential gradual switch from fossil fuels to renewable energy will help combat climate change. Using renewable power sources in a decentralized system specifically provides benefits simply because the power is consumed close to where it is created. This includes solar, wind, geothermals, and hydropower.

Solar energy technology is still developing: Because solar power is not as widely used and developed as other energy production systems like fossil fuels, there is room to develop decentralized solar power systems without dismantling the systems that are already in place.

Cons to decentralized solar energy

High up-front costs: Even though the costs of renewable energy sources are decreasing, there is still a lot of money that goes into setting up a decentralized system. A 5 kW system ($3/W) would cost approximately $16000 on average to install on the roof of a personal household (Brill, 2023). This high up-front cost is a big deterrent for potential users and is a big problem in terms of accessibility. If a switch was made to decentralized solar energy for a larger community, government money could be used to support this transition, but policymakers would have to agree and implement this new system. Additionally, whether or not maintenance service fees are covered will be a big driver of decentralized solar energy system adoptions – especially at the household level. However, this disadvantage can become less of an issue as the solar energy industry expands, and the cost will decline over time.

Perpetuation of the energy poverty cycle: In order to transition from a centralized (and often non-renewable) energy source to a decentralized solar energy system, there is the issue of potentially perpetuating the energy poverty cycle. Government policy makers are met with difficult decisions in terms of who they should prioritize to receive these new systems and who are left in the dark (literally). This can come from geographical constraints, as more rural and remote communities with a smaller population may not be prioritized. Additionally, the free distribution of solar power systems to rural and below-poverty communities could bring up complex political and technical issues. Overall, handouts of decentralized solar simply cannot end the cycle of rural energy poverty like it is often advertised. Additionally, decentralized energy is often not subsidized by the government, and so funding can become a problem (especially for poorer regions) since off-grid power is currently mostly provided by smaller companies ("Planning Energy Access: Centralized or Decentralized Electrification"). This could perpetuate the unequal distribution of power due to poverty.

Supply mismatch: Because electricity produced by solar radiation is dependent on the weather and time of day, supply mismatch issues can arise. This is due to the difference between hourly curves in energy generation and of energy uptake. This implies that adequate storage is needed if the energy generated is not consumed straight away. This would require batteries. Batteries can also pose an additional environmental risk due to their often-inadequate disposal ("Planning Energy Access: Centralized or Decentralized Electrification"). Not suitable for large industries, like agriculture: While the method of generating power through a decentralized solar system can provide many benefits for households with low power needs, it may be inappropriate for industry or agriculture. "In such scenarios, grid-based access might be needed to transition to efficient electric pumps for better irrigation, which will produce higher farm incomes, or for setting up small-scale industries and other income-generating activities from home that will require more power" ("Planning Energy Access: Centralized or Decentralized Electrification"). In these scenarios, implementing a decentralized system may be inadequate. These systems are sometimes considered a "pre-grid electrification option" that is more useful for lower levels of electricity consumption such as household lighting, TV viewing, running of appliances, and other daily household needs. ("Planning Energy Access: Centralized or Decentralized Electrification"). Industries like agriculture rely on more abundant power sources, and so a decentralized system may not work.

Loss of efficient regulation: With centralized energy systems, it is easier to manage and control. With decentralization, control is spread out and diluted, which could cause some issues.

Importance of decentralized solar energy

In addition to all the benefits of decentralized solar power in comparison to centralized, decentralized solar energy has an environmental benefit, and is also a solution to bring power to rural, isolated, and developing areas. There is a massive lack of access to electricity in much of the developing world. Many places in Africa, Asia, and Central America would be good candidates for decentralized solar power systems, as they receive much sunlight year-round due to being close to the equator.

Decentralizing solar power systems is one step in the right direction in terms of sustainability. As technology progresses, the power systems that have been used for decades have increasing and worsening flaws and have numerous negative impacts on the planet in terms of climate change. With decentralization of solar energy, a door is opened for homes to become more self-sustaining and environmentally friendly. Our current use of fossil fuels is unsustainable, and so a switch to solar power (specifically, decentralized solar power) is a good solution that is long-lasting, efficient, and sustainable.

With the centralized system we have in place now, there is a lot of energy insecurity that carries a massive economic and social cost. Power outages and grid issues are a consequence of energy overconsumption, providing more pressure on energy companies. If energy is decentralized, households and businesses will be able to self-supply their own energy, providing more security and independence.

Barriers to the implementation of decentralized solar power systems

Switching from a centralized solar power system to a decentralized one is not as easy as it sounds, as there is a requirement to overcome many obstacles. There needs to be support from policy makers, financial personnel, and institutional development. Especially in developing countries, there are more urgent problems that politicians pay attention to. In areas that rely on fossil fuels for electricity, lawmakers are usually hesitant to switch to a seemingly more expensive renewable energy strategy. Another barrier to decentralized solar power systems is their high up-front cost. Other barriers for the dissemination of decentralized solar power systems include lack of skilled people for maintenance and installation, unavailability of spare parts, lack of access and awareness, other financial priorities on the individual level, and lack of training. The infrastructure of many buildings is also a barrier to the installation of solar panels on roofs. Most of what is built today is designed to operate via fossil fuels and power lines. Many roofs were built without the intention of ever installing solar panels, and so some buildings and homes are not suitable environments for such technology. Finally, market entry is the last barrier to be discussed in this section. Since solar power in general is a newer technology, it must compete with well-established existing technologies. Because they are well-established, investors, politicians, and businesses invest heavily in these technologies, so they hold more market power. Overall, decentralized solar power has many advantages but would need to overcome numerous obstacles to be implemented in the future.

Example of a decentralized renewable energy model (Lebanon):
In Lebanon, the majority of households pay 2 electrical bills: a low bill for unreliable energy, and an additional high bill for a supplementary private generator. Lebanon is highly dependent on fuel imports, and they have a centralized power system that is intertwined with government issues, and this is reflected on the power system, as it is based on "confessional power-sharing that safeguards the interests of the different political leaders". A transition to decentralized power, specifically a clean power source like solar, could circumvent these political obstacles, reduce the cost of electricity, and reduce the reliance on import fuel. In Lebanon, the impacts of having a centralized power system cause a lot of injustice based on geographical location. The farther a household resides from the capital of Beirut, any blackouts that occur last longer and the cost of generator power is more. These distance households also have a consistently lower utility supply of power, simply because they are situated far from the central power source. Implementing a decentralized system could increase economic growth (because reliable electricity is a main driver of this), and lead to a more reliable energy source. There would be a barrier as this conversion would challenge the current government policies and structure, and would decrease political involvement. Solar would be a good choice for the source of energy, as Lebanon as the majority of the days are sunny, and an abundance of energy can be generated with ease. Other benefits to this system is the creation of jobs (help recover from unemployment due to the pandemic), and this model would not be too difficult to deploy. This solution could be applied to other nations that have similar energy-related issues, such as Jordan (Obeid, 2021)

Is a centralized/decentralized combination possible?
Because both decentralized and centralized power systems have pros and cons, it may be possible to adopt a combination, either to act as a transition from centralization to decentralization, or as a more permanent solution. There could be a central plant that provides smaller and distributed plants with additional energy (the small plants also generate their own energy). The smaller plants

supply energy directly to consumers. This would combine the advantages of having energy production in proximity to consumers with the advantage of having a central plant that coordinates the others. This system not only applies to energy distribution but is also a strategy for the distribution of goods.

Conclusion:

In conclusion, the decentralization of energy systems in general have both advantages and disadvantages. Specifically, solar power is a sustainable system that could be relatively easily implemented in a decentralized fashion that can address many of the power generation and distribution problems that we face today. Access to energy and environmental sustainability are two of the main drivers of a potential transition from centralized to decentralized energy systems, and decisions to make widespread changes that benefit these two factors depends on government policy makers. Because many policy decisions are financially-driven, it is important to also highlight the economic advantages of a decentralized system (in certain circumstances and if appropriate) to encourage this transition.

References

"Barriers to Renewable Energy Technologies." Union of Concerned Scientists, https://www.ucsusa.org/resources/barriers-renewable-energy-technologies

Quoilin S, Orosz M. 2013. Rural Electrification through Decentralized Concentrating Solar Power: Technological and Socio-Economic Aspects. Journal of Sustainable Development of Energy, Water and Environment Systems, 1(3): 199-212.
http://www.sdewes.org/jsdewes/pi2013.01.0015

D'Agostino AL, Lund PD, Urpelainen J. 2016. The Business of Distributed Solar Power: a Comparative Case Study of Centralized Charging Stations and Solar Microgrids. WIREs Energy and Environment, 5(6): 640-648.
https://wires.onlinelibrary.wiley.com/doi/full/10.1002/wene.209?casa_token=5zyED1CEJg0AAAAA%3AE2UBFoDXK6tovkv3ylShGRO3qLlZTKYgFVjJXvq-LFBeJG4KwsgEOUM513eRv3-f_emnxzFwDZraM2xjTw

Ecker F, Hahnel UJJ, Spada H. 2017. Promoting Decentralized Sustainable Energy Systems in Different Supply Scenarios: The Role of Autarky Aspiration. Frontiers in Energy Research, 5.
https://www.frontiersin.org/articles/10.3389/fenrg.2017.00014/full

Gupta A. 2014. Centralized Solar Energy Versus Captive Solar Power: Why Small is Big in Solar. Renewable Energy World.
https://www.renewableenergyworld.com/solar/centralized-solar-energy-versus-captive-solar-power-why-small-is-big-in-solar/

"Solar Energy." National Geographic.
https://education.nationalgeographic.org/resource/solar-energy

Newton E. 2021. What are the Pros and Cons of Centralized and Decentralized Distribution?
https://parcelindustry.com/article-5707-What-Are-the-Pros-and-Cons-of-Centralized-and-Decentralized-Distribution.html#:~:text=1%20•Increased%20operational%20costs%20and%20for%20multiple%20facilities,efficient%20inventory%20management%20and%20higher%20minimum%20stocks%20required

Yassin L, Wyns A. 2017. The Importance of Decentralized Solar Energy. Ecologist.
https://theecologist.org/2017/oct/19/importance-decentralised-solar-energy

"Decentralized Renewable Energy Systems: A Status-Quo Analysis." Advanced Science News. 2021
https://www.advancedsciencenews.com/decentralized-renewable-energy-systems-a-status-quo-analysis/

"Decentralized Renewable Energy for Improving Energy Access in the LDCs." 2019.
https://climate.mit.edu/posts/decentralized-renewable-energy-improving-energy-access-ldcs

"Solar Power Guide."
https://solarpower.guide/who-invented-solar-power

Yadav P, Davies PJ, Sarkodie SA. 2019. The Prospects of Decentralised Solar Energy Home Systems in Rural Communities: User Experience, Determinants, and Impact of Free Solar Power on the Energy Poverty Cycle. Energy Strategy Reviews, 26.
https://www.sciencedirect.com/science/article/pii/S2211467X19301166

"Planning Energy Access: Centralized or Decentralized Electrification." https://energypedia.info/wiki/Planning_energy_access:_Centralized_or_decentralized_electrification

Zweibel K. 2013. "Harnessing Solar Power: The Photovoltaics Challenge."

"How Does Solar Work?". https://www.energy.gov/eere/solar/how-does-solar-work

Ritchie H, Roser M, Rosado P. 2022. "Energy." https://ourworldindata.org/energy

https://www.ey.com/en_pt/recai/can-decentralized-energy-get-good-enough-fast-enough

Church B. 2022. "How Long Do Solar Panels Last?" https://www.consumeraffairs.com/solar-energy/how-long-do-solar-panels-last.html

Brill R. 2023. "How Much do Solar Panels Cost?" Forbes Home. https://www.forbes.com/home-improvement/solar/cost-of-solar-panels/

Obeid J. 2021. "Failure to Power: The Need for Decentralized Renewable Energy Models." CSIS.
https://www.csis.org/analysis/failure-power-need-decentralized-renewable-energy-models

Ohiare S. 2013. Rural Electrification Through Decentralized Off-Grid Systems in Developing Countries. Academia.https://www.academia.edu/3235570/Rural_Electrification_Through_Decentralised_Off_grid_Systems_in_Developing_Countries Chapter 9

Chapter 10
Decentralized Hydro

Alex Abraha

The location of energy producing facilities closer to the location of energy consumption defines a decentralized hydro system. A high-speed Decentralized Exchange can be built using the open-source framework called Hydro. Developers who want to create decentralized exchanges without having to deal with the difficulty and cost of creating, implementing, and securing smart contracts can use Hydro. A new decentralized exchange must be built from the ground up, which is quite expensive and time consuming.

Hydro significantly reduces the time and expense through: The Hydro SDK, which sends a single docker command to launch an entire and readily customisable Decentralized Exchange interface. The Hydro API is open source and standardized, as well. DeFi projects and many users are already completely integrated. Smart contracts for decentralized exchange that are effective, secure, and versatile. No token holding requirements or weird token fees: complete freedom for Relayers.

The main project consists of a set of open - sourced smart contracts and parts for providing functionalities for quick, safe, and efficient ERC20 token exchanges. Building on Hydro offers not only a great opportunity to learn and grow in one of the hottest areas of technology, but you can also create a system that can generate income. Trading commissions and the Hydro Protocol Economic Incentives are two ways that Hydro Relayers naturally make money (if you choose to opt-in). Participants in the Hydro Economics are automatically given HOT tokens (explained in more detail in the hydro-token section) in proportion to the quantity of deals they complete. Renewable energy is often used as the primary source in hybrid and decentralized renewable energy systems, with backup provided by batteries and/or diesel generators (DGs).

To keep the stability of the energy supply, decentralized renewable energy systems are hybridized. Such systems are desirable for ensuring rural areas have access to power because of their dependability and affordability. Numerous studies have been conducted to address techno-economic optimization for the proper use of renewable energy sources. Even though various research has concentrated on hybrid technology applications for renewable energy sources and their optimization, there is still a severe lack of adequate energy solutions for off-grid photovoltaic (PV) systems linked with storage units and DGs.

The majority of previous research has solely been concerned with reducing the hybrid system's overall cost. Such evaluations disregard the interaction between the location of a hybrid system and the particular energy technology of optimal scale, which has a considerable impact on installation and operating choices. Therefore, particular energy technologies combined with backup from batteries and/or DGs are a potential choice to enhance energy availability in cases of rural areas of developing countries where grid expansion is not feasible in the next 10-15 years . In Sweden, a comparable study was carried out on the techno-economic examination of off-grid technology. The study came to the conclusion that the usage of off-grid technologies and associated mini-grids was influenced by the greater expenditure in grid expansion. Homer Pro (a hybrid optimization model for multiple energy resources) and MATLAB (a matrix laboratory) have both been used in studies on cost optimization for power demand. Energy system optimization contributes to a reliable and profitable supply.

A decrease in revenue generating results from an unstable electrical supply. This demonstrates the significance of optimizing energy systems. A strategy for applying fast resource evaluation for planning rural electrification in Zambia was offered in the United States Agency for International Development (USAID) study report [15, 16]. Mahapatra and Dasappa [17] have already used and presented this methodology. They used the model to determine whether decentralized renewable energy systems for rural areas might provide better energy options than grid expansion. The analytical model evaluates the life-cycle costs (LCC) of various accessible energy systems and looks at the economic distance limit (EDL) from the current grid access point. The LCC aids in choosing a technological choice for electrification that is most cost-effective among the various options whereas the EDL aids in comparing the economic distance between decentralized energy systems and grid expansion. The LCC of off-grid energy technologies and the LCC of grid expansion were calculated and compared by Sinha and Kandpal [18–20].

Under typical geographic conditions, grid expansion is often found to be cost-effective; however, grid expansion is found to be less practical in remote locations due to challenging geographical topography. Nouni et alstudy .'s [21] compared the cost of energy from available off-grid solutions with the cost of energy access from expanding the grid. According to the study, there are numerous locations where expanding the grid is more expensive than providing off-grid energy access, depending on accessibility and technical challenges. The Government of Nepal (GoN) has given off-grid energy technologies top priority in its development goals due to its accessibility to energy and dependability. The GoN has prioritized effective energy use to enhance rural livelihoods in addition to promoting energy availability. The Alternative Energy Promotion Centre (AEPC) has assisted rural communities in installing more than 1000 micro/pico hydropower plants with capacities of under 100 kW, resulting in a total installation of more than 20 MW, ensuring the access to electricity for more than 200 000 households [22]. The state-owned energy monopoly Nepal Electricity Authority (NEA) is expanding its grid to electrify rural areas on a huge scale. NEA produced 2308.37 GWh of power in total during the 2017–18 fiscal year (FY). Due to the increasing demand for energy, the NEA generation was unable to meet it during this time period; as a result, 2581.80 GWh of power was imported from India.

The fundamental issue in the energy systems that is causing limited access to energy is a lack of coordinated planning. 9.3% of Nepal's entire population does not have any access to electricity, according to a recent World Bank (WB) report . Grid connection, the most popular method of energy access, provides less dependable electricity because more than 60% of Nepal's population lives in steep, sparsely inhabited areas, making it challenging to guarantee energy access through the national grid. In this context, energy access through isolated renewable-energy systems may be the best solution. But there are numerous issues in isolated renewable-energy systems such as the periodic nature of renewable energy sources, high installation and operating costs, poor reliability, low load factor, maintenance and monitoring activities. To solve these issues, techno-economic optimization with the proper design of an energy system will be instrumental. An isolated hybrid energy system may be a better option to provide a reliable energy system by minimizing issues associated with energy systems.

The central grid, isolated local energy sources, and hybrid technologies can all be used to electrify rural areas. Given these options, the current study concentrates on each of the three choices for dependable energy access. The economic viability and resources available locally determine the preferred technology. The grid-expansion option is compared in this analysis to possible isolated and hybrid energy systems. Different off-grid arrangements are evaluated technologically and economically, and their viability is extensively explored. The proposed systems' commercial viability is assessed through comparison with life-cycle and energy costs. Better energy planning is projected to benefit from this comprehensive analysis.

In developing countries like Nepal, there are two options for electrification. Understandably, national grid expansion is the first and foremost option, but it may not be a viable option due to the high upfront cost. In such cases, decentralized energy systems could be the most suitable alternatives, even for long-term options. The options should be technically and financially compared for the selection of better choices between off-grid electrification and grid expansion. In developing countries, micro-hydropower (MHP), solar PV, DG and backups (battery and DG) are the major and viable off-grid technologies used for energy access. In Nepal as well, these technologies are widespread. In Nepal, ~3000 MHP projects contributing ~35 MW of electricity have been installed. More than 600 000 household-level solar PV systems with battery-backup systems and 1500 units of the institutional solar PV plant are already installed.

Another advantage of decentralized hydropower is that it is a relatively low-impact form of energy generation. Unlike large hydroelectric dams, which can have significant environmental impacts on the surrounding area, decentralized hydro systems are typically much smaller in scale and therefore have a much lower environmental impact. This can include reducing greenhouse gas emissions, protecting local wildlife, and preserving natural habitats. One of the most common forms of decentralized hydro power is micro-hydro power. This type of hydroelectric system is typically used to generate electricity for a single building or small community. Micro-hydro systems are typically powered by small streams or rivers, and can be as small as a few hundred watts up to a few hundred kilowatts. Micro-hydro systems are relatively simple to install, and can often be done using off-the-shelf components.

Another form of decentralized hydro power is pico-hydro power. Pico-hydro systems are similar to micro-hydro systems, but are even smaller in scale. They are typically used to power a single household or small business, and can be as small as a few watts. Pico-hydro systems are often powered by small streams or waterfalls, and can be installed using a variety of different components. Decentralized hydro power can also be used to power entire communities. Community-scale hydro systems are typically larger than micro-hydro or pico-hydro systems and can be used to generate electricity for a small village or town. Community-scale hydro systems can be powered by small rivers or streams and can be as large as a few hundred kilowatts.

Are decentralized energy resources the future of electricity?

Decentralized energy resources from a business perspective
Decentralized energy resources (DERs) were defined by Paul Grod, president and chief executive officer of Rodan Energy, to more accurately reflect what they encompass. He emphasized that DERs enable consumers to engage in marketplaces that were previously accessible exclusively to generators while highlighting a number of benefits for consumers. A DER-based electricity grid is also more affordable, durable, adaptable, and clean, according to Grod. The financial incentives to reduce peak loads, the need to lessen power disruptions, and the rise in demand for electricity from important businesses are all factors that have contributed to the DER market expansion in Ontario and other jurisdictions during the past ten years. Overall, according to Grod, DERs are the way of the future for electricity, but he cautions that baseload power will still be required and that large-scale infrastructure for nuclear, hydro, and wind energy

is best suited to centralized power. Future market drivers for DER adoption will mostly be ancillary service revenues and transmission and distribution costs.

Bringing public and private sectors together in decentralized energy resources

Participants heard an overview of the duties and responsibilities of the independent Electricity System Operator (IESO) from Patrick Lo, Senior Manager of Partnerships in Innovation, Research, and Development. According to the IESO, technical viability, financial sources, operations, procurement procedures, process understanding and education, technology maturity, and costs are the main obstacles to non-wires alternatives and DERs. The research and white papers are the first steps in the IESO's innovation roadmap. Then come capital projects and process improvements, demonstration and evaluation projects, and lastly partnerships and capability building. The IESO's Non-Wires Alternatives Demonstration Project, which was sponsored with assistance from Natural Resources Canada and provided by Alectra Utilities, was described by Lo as he wrapped up his remarks. The project is located in York Region, where the demand for power is anticipated to increase beyond the capacity of the system.

Lessons from the U.S.

Associate Professor of Economics David Brown at the University of Alberta used examples from the U.S. to analyze the problems with net metering and the discussions around the creation of retail rates. Behind-the-meter DER production is frequently compensated at the current retail rate, which can result in over- or under compensation of distributed solar and other DERs, worries about cost-shifting, issues with rate design, and a bad mismatch with the real costs of energy services. In order to illustrate a retail rate design based on the value "stack," which totals the potential worth of DERs (i.e., energy, generation capacity, environmental value, and transmission and distribution capacity) depending on one's location, Brown utilized the example of New York. The advantages of this architecture include less cost-shifting, capacity metrics that can represent local restrictions, and better estimated values and prices of DERs. Although the design smoothes out too much and locks in rates for up to 25 years, it also involves complex and contentious valuations. According to

Brown, the main issues going forward will be balancing economic efficiency and fairness, mapping simulated benefits and costs, providing information and transparency on the grid-value and costs of DERs, and recovering stranded costs.

Energy liberation: decentralized energy systems coming our way?
In supposedly industrialized nations, centralized electricity systems have become standard since the second world war. Regardless of the energy source, they are built around massive power plants that enable economies of scale and ease the distribution of electricity. The widespread adoption of renewable energy sources and the introduction of smart grids, however, have exposed this tried-and-true model to new decentralized competition.

Imagine with the former a number of smaller-scale energy production sites, such as home solar systems and nearby wind turbines (on a neighborhood or municipality level). With the latter, however, the impossible becomes possible since it is now possible to manage a decentralized network, which is an incredibly difficult operation. Both are influenced by social movements that promote both new energy independence and cleaner, more regional energy sources.

Your own personal profitable technology?
Decentralization has long been constrained by the prohibitive yields of solar and wind energy, but it is now gaining ground as a result of a sharp decline in prices. According to a recent iClimatearth study that uses California as a case study, a self-sufficient electrical energy home (with an electric automobile) results in annual savings of $7,641 when compared to a standard gas-heated home. According to IRENA (the International Renewable Energy Agency), between 2010 and 2020, solar energy costs decreased by 85%. The rising cost of electricity is another factor that encourages self-consumption. In France, 100,000 houses were linked to the network in 2021, up from 14,000 in 2017. This demand does however bring up the issue of the necessary upfront expenditure, which is likely to favor the wealthiest households and widen the energy difference. Even though 6.5 million families in the UK are experiencing fuel poverty, the market for solar panels is growing.

Developing countries shunning centralization?

Decentralized networks can assist locals in poor nations, especially in Africa where access to power is still far from universal, by providing local-level structuring and assisting them in getting around frequently inefficient local authorities. A newly formed citizens' effort for renewable energy goes in this direction in Nigeria, where the electrical grid covers 60% of the nation. In Ghana, Guinea, Ethiopia, Kenya, Nigeria, and Tunisia, the African Development Bank recently invested $164 million to create decentralized renewable energy. However, there is still a tonne of space for improvement: Africa generates about 5TWh of solar energy annually, out of a potential of over 60 million.

Local ownership on the up

In addition to self-consumption, energy decentralization can be supported by strong community logic, which encourages the establishment of regional "microgrids" that can cater to particular regional demands. The State of the Energy Union report states that 7,700 energy communities in the EU, made up of at least 2 million members, provide 7% of the EU's renewable energy. A map of the French energy environment was made by Energie Partagée at the same time, showing the range of projects implemented, from photovoltaic farms in the Pyrenees to a hydroelectric facility in the Cévennes.

A small digital revolution

An increase in data and AI integration in a decentralized energy management system always results in new software requirements. The DERMS (Distributed Energy Resources Management System) system fosters genuine competition among the key market participants. In order to add more than 1,000 GWh of distributed and renewable electricity resources to the grid over the next ten years, Schneider Electrics just bought Autogrid. Leading companies in a market expected to reach $23 billion by 2026 include GE Digital and Siemens. Digital solutions are also being developed for people (and businesses) who produce new energy. Blockchain was used in an experiment at ETH Zurich in Switzerland to enable peer-to-peer energy trading. Self-consumption management systems like MyLight Systems, which are less futuristic, are already in the works.

Storage capacities and two-way networks
Intelligent network management cannot solve the storage problem, which is crucial for overcoming renewable energy's sporadic nature and preventing "waste". The development of batteries for individual users, such as Tesla's Powerwall and entire solutions (panels, storage, software) from enphase, is a result of decentralized energy networks. Network providers are also participating, as shown by RTE's Ringo project, which involves setting up a sizable battery network to handle intermittency. A surge in multidirectional V2G (or vehicle-to-grid) connectors, like those made by Nuvee, which convert vehicle batteries into network-wide storage capacity, is another indication of the growing popularity of electric mobility.

Decentralized Renewables & The Rise of the Micro-Enterprise Economy
Decentralized renewable energy has historically been undervalued in developing countries since it is thought that it can only provide electricity for domestic usage, and then primarily for minimal illumination. The concept of "productive use," which involves directly or indirectly producing things and services to generate revenue or value, has proven to be more difficult. However, the truth is that decentralized technologies like microgrids have long been used to power enterprises in remote regions of China, Australia, and the United States, while micro-hydro is a cornerstone of the rural economy in Nepal. Even the smallest solar lights are used to power mobile phone charging businesses, brighten stores, and assist farmers with tending to their livestock. Numerous businesses are currently stepping up their drive toward solutions for productive use as a result of the market's rapid expansion and growing investment in decentralized renewables. As a result, a "Micro-Enterprise Economy" is emerging. The mini-grid firm Steamaco has also realized the exceptional opportunity it has to more actively increase productivity as a result of its experience powering convenience stores, cold storage, welding, repair shops, water pumps, and more.

References

https://www.renewableenergyworld.com/storage/decentralized-renewables-the-rise-of-the-micro-enterprise-economy/#gref

https://academic.oup.com/ce/article/5/4/690/6408720

https://www.researchgate.net/publication/229045728_Micro-hydropower_A_promising_decentralized_renewable_technology_and_its_impact_on_rural_livelihoods

https://www.frontiersin.org/articles/10.3389/fenrg.2017.00014/full

Chapter 11
Barriers to Change: The Forces Keeping Decentralized Energy Away

Michelle Reinink

Readiness for change?
The benefits of decentralized energy systems are vast and various. However, implementing these systems can prove to be difficult due to specific barriers that arise when attempting to develop these projects and unfortunately prevent positive change. Centralized or traditional energy systems have been capitalizing on the energy market in many countries up to date and this can be highlighted by the factors that inhibit the proposal, acceptance, and follow through for using decentralized systems. This may be in part due to the governing bodies that regulate energy production, taking advantage of cheaper alternatives in spite of progressive possibilities that decentralized services could provide (Ha and Kumar, 2). These factors are not limited to a few specific reasons, but rather cover a broad array of complications that inhibit the evolution of decentralized energy.

Although there are many factors that impede the development of these systems, one of the most significant is a lack of awareness about decentralized energy, first and foremost, but also little to no knowledge of the benefits and investment opportunities that they provide. The cost required to build and operate decentralized energy systems can seem drastically higher than traditional systems at first, with longer waiting periods for return on investments, thus requiring patience for longer term payouts (Zyadin, Halder, Kahkonen, Puhakka,86). Decentralized systems can also be more complex than centralized systems in that they require newer technologies and the level of complexity in operating and maintaining decentralized systems increases in correlation with this. Complexity of these systems has been shown to necessitate feelings of inadequacies in terms of the benefits of decentralized energy as well as the notion that they may be too complicated for individuals attempting to utilize them (Reddy, Painuly, 1436). Along with a lack of awareness, feelings of cynicism for decentralized energy systems have proven to inhibit their widespread implementation. A lack of general awareness by the public and investors, regulations restricting their implementation, topography, and perceived inconvenience of these systems are also considered barriers (Beck, Martinot, 366). For the promotion and inclusion of decentralized energy systems in societies, these barriers each need to be addressed. However, they should not be taken as standalone factors. Rather, they should be looked at as cyclical concerns that arise and lay premise for each other. Each should be seen as correlated with another, and in turn affecting one will have an impact on the others. For instance, the awareness of benefits of decentralized energy may be lost in the complexities, therefore, investors may be less motivated to provide funding which in turn leads to the higher costs. Or the complexity in the necessitation for utilization of greater resources lends to higher cost of producing operating systems.

Lack of awareness

The first barrier, perhaps the most important, is the lack of awareness of these systems. The promotion of information for these systems could increase public support for decentralized projects. Knowledge of the benefits may incentivise societies to turn to these systems rather than relying solely on centralized energy systems. Additionally, providing accessible information to the public may also lead to an increase in investors willing to sponsor the development of such projects. Without proper knowledge on how these systems are built, operated, and the benefits or potential drawbacks, investors are going to be less motivated to pursue funding these projects. A lack of awareness for decentralized energy projects has been shown to necessitate feelings of inadequacies about these systems from the general public, as well as a misunderstanding of the benefits that they have as well as the notion that they may be too complex for individuals attempting to utilize them (Reddy, Painuly, 1437). Along with a lack of awareness, feelings of cynicism for decentralized energy systems has proven to inhibit their widespread implementation, this is most likely due to prior knowledge of the implementation of past decentralized projects that had failed; these failures may in turn lead to a lack of faith in the functionality of these systems (Yaqoot, Diwan, and Kandpal, 479). Familiarity with operation and function will increase the users overall comfort level, however, with the less information available for these systems, individuals are less likely to view these projects as beneficial (Beck, Martinot, 367). Ambiguity of decentralized system performance and perceived complexity of use promotes these negative perceptions and households are more likely to continue utilizing centralized energy systems.

The question that should be answered then, in terms of gaining more public acceptance, is what would motivate users to switch from systems they are already familiar with when decentralized systems seem confusing and with less short term gain? A lack of awareness will influence perceptions, decrease investments, and lower public motivation to promote decentralized energy and this in turn leads to negative perceptions (Reddy, Painuly, 1437). It cannot necessarily be said that this lack of awareness is due to public ignorance or refusal to learn about these systems in the absence of proper information. Therefore, if public information were to be promoted on the benefits of these systems along with why others have failed in the past and a plan to prevent future failures, public support may increase. Awareness alone may not be the determining factor for greater investments, Faiers and Neame state that it is also the perception and attitudes of the public that sway their decisions in supporting these projects, and use an example of driving an electric car based on the belief that you are reducing your carbon footprint instead of wanting to drive something for speed or sport (1799). According to Faiers and Neame, attitudes may be negative in regards to general feelings of efficacy for renewable systems and therefore, though knowledge may be readily available, the failure to believe that these systems will be a good investment long-term may be just as detrimental as having no information at all (1799). This highlights the next barrier for change commonly discussed in regards to utilizing decentralized energy: the implementation of these programs requires extensive funding. Not only for operation but for accessibility of information on these systems for the public. Without funding, companies associated with decentralized energy systems are less able to provide access to greater information, therefore limiting the amount of investment in their companies.

Costs for the implementation of decentralized systems

The costs of decentralized energy systems can seem daunting, especially in a projects initial stages. This is because the required investments include several factors such as funding research for the project, purchasing the equipment, paying for the construction, staffing, finding proper permits and paying for their operations and general maintenance (Beck, Martinot, 366). Initial investment costs for these programs can be high and the monetary return for these systems is oftentimes uncertain because they are not as well established as centralized energy services (Zyadin, Halder, Kahkonen, Puhakka, 86). In comparison to decentralized energy systems, centralized systems are provided greater subsidies that lower the cost for individual usage: for instance, an annual budget of between 100 to 200 billion dollars is provided by the World Bank and International Energy Agency for centralized systems on an annual term, whereas decentralized energy systems may not have access to the same amount of funding, giving tradition fuel systems an advantage in lower production and operating fees (Beck, Martinot, 366). This is perhaps due, in part, to the longevity of established centralized energy programs. Costs can also create uneven distribution in terms of where these systems are utilized and the regulations informing on what type of energy systems can be acquired in which regions, leading to a capitalism of specific energy systems for a given area (Altmann, et al., 64). As an example, the cost of repairing a system utilizing solar energy has been cited at approximately 4 times higher than that of conventional energy systems as well as higher start-up fees for the projects leading to a longer wait in payouts for investors (Ozsabuncuoglu, 758). One way to assist in removing this barrier is to provide information and analysis on total life-cycle costs of these projects as this is where the cost comparison can be truly made with other, centralized energy sources (Beck, Martinot, 367). For instance, with the utilization of different elements for energy production, decentralized systems do not procure the same cost that fuel-based centralized systems do and avoid a potential climb in cost associated with fuel consumption making it perhaps a more cost-effective investment long-term (Beck, Martinot, 367), however, this may not be known to future investors, therefore continuing to limit the amount of funding and perpetuating a lack of knowledge provided on these systems. If decentralized energy systems had access to the market in the same way that centralized services have been able to capitalize, these programs may gain traction in procuring funding and investors to increase their adoption (Yaqoot, Diwan, and Kandpal 481). Other ways in which the cost barrier can be reduced for example, is increased research on developing more efficient technologies and equipment (Yaqoot, Mohammed, Diwan, and Kandpal, 486). However, the complexities of these systems both in terms of technology and operation, may create barriers in the attempt to lower costs. A more complex system may mean a more costly system.

Complexities of decentralized systems

The technological intricacies of these systems work in tangent with the other barriers exemplified above in that it may be harder to inform the public on complex systems in ways that allow for complete understanding. This may require extensive presentation of information about decentralized services and therefore, increase costs for marketing. In addition, the costs required to produce and maintain these systems will also be greater due to the elaborate nature of repair and maintenance; a case study conducted by Ha and Kumar, in Nepal looked at the functionality of renewable energy services approximately two years after they were constructed (4). This study found that 56% of the services were no longer in working order while less than 10% were functioning perfectly, highlighting the need for consistent maintenance to ensure ideal performance (4). This adds to the problems concerning technological intricacies of these projects as decentralized energy systems can also often host complexities in their management and often require individuals with specific training and knowledge to ensure they are operated properly as seen as a barrier in the implementation of programs in China, for example (Junfeng, Li,Runqing, Zhengmin, Jingli,& Yangin, 19). Yaqoot, Diwan, and Kandpal, cite that decentralized energy projects have often failed because their technology was too complex (479). Nasirov, Shahriyar, Silva, and. Agostini state that there are complexities in finding storage for the electrical energy production of decentralized services (92). Additionally, renewable systems for electrical energy increase in complexity at the level of connecting resource to individual users as cited in the European Parliment's Internal Policy (59).

The improvements of modern day technologies are impressive and beneficial, however, if systems become too intricate and advanced in nature, then there is greater necessity to offer training programs to operate and maintain these projects. However, in terms of grid stability, there are strategies that can be utilized to ensure performance and reliability: using active network management, increased coordination between transmission and distribution systems, and improved monitoring and control systems (Chowdhury, Chowdhury, S. P.,Crossley, 988).

In this sense, a question that should be heavily considered is: are these systems less reliable than traditional, centralized systems? This question has the capacity to increase the likelihood for apprehensive feelings towards investment and support for these systems due to the necessary elemental conditions for the production of energy services (Yaqoot, Diwan, Kandpal, 478). Therefore, the engineering of these systems should promote an ability to overcome inconsistent environmental actors to maintain a constant energy source.

Additionally, decentralized systems may already have an advantage in utilizing greater area per system due to different systems utilizing different types of topography as they are not limited to utilizing on central grid per se (Yaqoot, Diwan, and Kandpal, 478), however, there is also a benefit to the advancement in utilizing artificial intelligence and analytic techniques in tracking any grid malfunctions and ensuring proper maintenance (Bashir, Khan, Prabadevi, Deepa, Alnumay, Gadekallu, & Maddikunta)

Topographical considerations for decentralized energy systems

The geographical features of a landscape can be described as its topography. The topography of a landscape has important implications for the development of energy systems including the ability to construct these projects as well as operate them within a stable environment. This is especially true in looking at city versus rural landscapes. For instance, a study conducted in Hong Kong found that placing solar energy panels on the buildings in a highrise district within the city had proven to be a challenging feat due to locationary features (Zhang,Shen, and Chan, 242). In addition, another study that was conducted in Great Britain found that wind projects proposed in places with nice scenery, the presence of such projects had a higher likelihood of being rejected (Weinand, McKenna, Kleinebrahm, Scheller, & Fichtner, 100301)

Another study conducted in Indonesia found a biogas project unsuccessful because building these projects on rice fields was considered taboo (Yaqoot, Diwan, and Kandpal, 484). Therefore, cultural expectations should be taken in tangent with topographical considerations when planning these projects in order to access the best geographical locations while respecting culture. One limitation that topography can present is resource availability. For example, solar panels require sunlight to produce energy and therefore cannot be located in an area where sunlight is restricted, for optimal energy production, they also need to be tilted in certain directions and thus, rely on prime topographical locations (Yunus Khan, Soudagar, Kanchan, Afzal, Banapurmath, Akram, & Shahapurkar, 512). Turbines requirement for wind may be faced with challenges if the location it is placed in has environmental features that prevent direct air flow such as other trees, and it is recommended that turbines be placed in locations away from other obstacles (El-Ahmar, Abou-Hashema El-Sayed, & Hemeida, 1475). This could be seen in cases where earthquakes or landslides occur frequently. If you place these systems in areas affected by natural disasters, the likelihood of damage to these systems is high, therefore increasing cost for labor and maintenance as well. Though the geographical features of a given location may pose difficulties in implementing decentralized projects, these systems may also have an advantage that other systems do not in that there are many different options that can utilize different environments where centralized systems may not have the same access, for instance solar energy may be beneficial for homes that cannot access the larger centralized grid energy as these systems can be expanded outside of centralized grids (Yaqoot, Diwan, and Kandpal, 478).

Resource Availability
Moreover, another barrier that may decrease acceptance and increase apprehensive feelings towards decentralized services pertains to the reliance of these systems on inconsistent elements for the production of energy, including wind for turbines, water for hydro dams, and sunlight for solar panels. Again, this is coupled with the geographical location of these systems and can be dependent on something as simple as they angle in which they are tilted, as seen with the direction of solar panels (El-Ahmar, Abou-Hashema, El-Sayed, and Hemeida, 1475). Because decentralized systems often rely on different elements, the availability of the elements for a given area must be taken into account when deciding where to build these projects and therefore, their capacity is contingent

on whether or not the specific resource being utilized is available (Beck, Martinot, 367). The availability of elements for the production of energy can also be seasonally dependent and therefore solutions will need to be discussed for regions with inconsistent weather patterns (Yaqoot, Diwan, and Kandpal, 478). Decentralized energy services therefore, stand a better chance of widespread implementation if prediciton methods are created for resource availability to mitigate the ability to store energy during times where they may be lacking (Altmann, Brenninkmeijer, Lanoix, Ellison, Crisan, Hugyecz, Koreneff, Hänninen, 60). Decentralized energy systems.

Governing Restrictions

The final barrier discussed, the governing bodies for these types of energy services. Additional consideration must also be given to the regulations placed on these systems and the framework in place for operating them, as this can determine whether the systems integration into a community will be successful or not (Ha and Kumar, 2). Ultimately, decentralized energy systems are complex and require a comprehensive and multidisciplinary approach to ensure their successful integration into the energy system.Another barrier that needs to be addressed in order to implement decentralized services is governing influences that make it difficult for these systems to gain accessibility and traction in progression. Ha and Kumar, cite that in terms of traditional centralized energy services, small groups of governing bodies typically hold capital on energy production and distribution for a given area, therefore potentially limiting the knowledge of the general public on information and that these governing bodies (2). It is not surprising that governing bodies will typically choose cheaper, established, centralized services in favor of attempting to develop newer, potentially more expensive services that encompass decentralized energy systems (Ha, Kumar, 2).

Conclusion

There are a lot of different factors that should be considered when attempting to move from centralized energy services to decentralized. These barriers should be addressed in full in order to allow for the smooth transition to these types of projects. Establishing these projects through to their completion lays host to a number of different challenges and barriers. Each of these barriers can be correlated with each other and therefore, each should be addressed to ease the process of transitioning. It all comes down to knowledge of these systems: knowledge of investment costs, the benefits, operations, technologies required, public usability and longevity of the system itself. With well provisioned information, the likelihood for public support, investors, and government approval should increase and assist in the removal of other barriers to follow. There are solutions to each of these preventative factors, such as suggestions for creating independent energy systems that have less government involvement so that the public has greater say in their implementation (Ha and Kumar, 2). If government systems can work in tangent with the public to decrease the barriers faced by decentralized systems, this could aid in their widespread implementation while allowing equal access.

References

Altmann, M., et al. "Decentralized energy systems." (2010).

Bashir, Ali K., et al. "Comparative Analysis of Machine Learning Algorithms for Prediction of Smart Grid Stability." International Transactions on Electrical Energy Systems, vol. 31, no. 9,
2021, pp. n/a.

Beck, Fredric, and Eric Martinot. Renewable Energy Policies and Barriers. vol. 5, Elsevier Inc,
2004, doi:10.1016/B0-12-176480-X/00488-5.

Bhattacharjee, Subhadeep, and Shantanu Acharya. "PV–wind hybrid power option for a low
wind topography." Energy Conversion and Management 89 (2015): 942-954.

Chowdhury, S. P., S. Chowdhury, and P. A. Crossley. "Islanding Protection of Active Distribution
Networks with Renewable Distributed Generators: A Comprehensive Survey." Electric Power
Systems Research, vol. 79, no. 6, 2009, pp. 984-992.

El-Ahmar, M. H., Abou-Hashema M. El-Sayed, and A. M. Hemeida.

"Evaluation of factors affecting wind turbine output power." 2017 Nineteenth International Middle East Power Systems Conference (MEPCON). IEEE, 2017.

Faiers, Adam, and Charles Neame. "Consumer Attitudes Towards Domestic Solar Power Systems." Energy Policy, vol. 34, no. 14, 2006, pp. 1797-1806.

Ha, Yoon-Hee, and Surya S. Kumar. "Investigating Decentralized Renewable Energy Systems Under Different Governance Approaches in Nepal and Indonesia: How does Governance Fail?" Energy Research & Social Science, vol. 80, 2021, pp. 102214.

Junfeng, Li, et al. "Policy Analysis of the Barriers to Renewable Energy Development in the People's Republic of China." Energy for Sustainable Development, vol. 6, no. 3, 2002, pp. 11-20.

Kabel, Tarek S., and Mohga Bassim. "Reasons for Shifting and Barriers to Renewable Energy: A Literature Review." International Journal of Energy Economics and Policy, vol. 10, no. 2, 2020, pp. 89-94. ProQuest https://www.proquest.com/scholarly-journals/reasons-shifting-barriers-renewable-energy/docview/2459596084/se-2.

Nasirov, Shahriyar, Carlos Silva, and Claudio A. Agostini. "Assessment of Barriers and Opportunities for Renewable Energy Development in Chile." Energy Sources. Part B, Economics, Planning and Policy, vol. 11, no. 2, 2016, pp. 150-156.

Ozsabuncuoglu, Ismail H. "Economic Analysis of Flat Plate Collectors of Solar Energy." Energy Policy, vol. 23, no. 9, 1995, pp. 755-763.

Painuly, J. P. "Barriers to Renewable Energy Penetration; a Framework for Analysis." Renewable Energy, vol. 24, no. 1, 2001, pp. 73-89.

Reddy, Sudhakar, and J. P. Painuly. "Diffusion of Renewable Energy Technologies: Barriers and Stakeholders' Perspectives." Renewable Energy, vol. 29, no. 9, 2004, pp. 1431-1447

Weinand, Jann M., et al. "The Impact of Public Acceptance on Cost Efficiency and Environmental Sustainability in Decentralized Energy Systems." Patterns (New York, N.Y.), vol. 2, no. 7, 2021, pp. 100301-100301.

Yaqoot, Mohammed, Parag Diwan, and Tara C. Kandpal. "Review of Barriers to the Dissemination of Decentralized Renewable Energy Systems." Renewable & Sustainable Energy Reviews, vol. 58, 2016, pp. 477-490.

Yunus Khan, T. M., et al. "Optimum location and influence of tilt angle on performance of solar PV panels." Journal of Thermal Analysis and Calorimetry 141 (2020): 511-532.

Zhang, Xiaoling, Liyin Shen, and Sum Y. Chan. "The Diffusion of Solar Energy use in HK: What are the Barriers?" Energy Policy, vol. 41, no. 1, 2012, pp. 241-249.

Zyadin, Anas, et al. "Challenges to Renewable Energy: A Bulletin of Perceptions from International Academic Arena." Renewable Energy, vol. 69, 2014, pp. 82-88

Overall Conclusion

Decentralized energy is a complex problem, requiring in depth analysis of all potential solutions and how to best implement this framework in a given region. The previous chapters look to introduce different concepts in a surface level to allow a baseline to decentralized energy. An understanding of what decentralization is, as well as the issues and challenges were presented. Different solutions to discrete problems were also introduced. Although there may be many solutions not covered, this book is meant to provide a start point for energy research.

Chapter 1 dealt with decentralized energy generation and the pros and cons of a decentralized energy grid. Decentralization was introduced as a method where energy is produced closer to the areas which it provides for. The solution is explored for its rapid response to changing factors, ability to have a flexible energy production source, such as renewables, and lead to lower efficiency drops.

Chapter 2 tackled the common problems of decentralization of energy and the intertwined issues that come with renewable energy. The chapter explored in detail different battery storage solutions to help mitigate the challenges of decentralization and renewable energy.

Chapter 3 described how smart grids are able to help mitigate challenges that arise through decentralization. Automation is explored and shown how it may be used to tackle efficiency and the balancing of power demands and supply. Smart girds are also used to better organize the distribution of energy produced. Chapter 4 explored the issues of decentralizing infrastructure. The chapter explores how old fossil fuel infrastructure can be retrofitted and adapted for renewable energy. Further the adaption of old infrastructure for a decentralized use was also explored.

Chapter 5 completes a detailed review of residual energy distribution, specifically on airplanes. A significant amount of heat is lost in airplane engines which running and is not recovered and used again. This chapter looks into the problems of excessive heat production in airplanes and the potential solutions to this problem.

Chapter 6 looks at residual energy distribution more generally and looks into the system of combined heat and power system, where excess heat energy is not wasted, but used for other productive purposes. The chapter also describes of examples of these systems being used and how a combined heat and energy system may be a solution for decentralization of energy.

Chapter 7 does a detailed dive into how cities, which has already transitioned to renewable energy, have achieved this feat. The chapter looks into the solutions of these cities and why renewable energy was so readily available to these geographic regions. The chapter also explores some of the political and ideological motivations for the transition to renewable energy. The chapter takes on two case studies which describes the unique geographic attributes which helped aid in its development of decentralized energy.

Chapter 8 looks into how wind power may be used to decentralized energy systems, and how this form of renewable energy is a suitable choice for the decentralization of energy systems. The ease, smoothness, and adaptability of wind turbines provides a great solution to rural communities and allows for production of energy to be more efficiently dissipated to these communities. Chapter 9, like chapter 8 looks into renewable energy production and how it is suitable for decentralization. However, this chapter focuses on solar energy production and how individuals and small groups may be able to use solar energy to decentralize the energy production in given regions. The cost, and ease of set up are explored and how the individual may be the driving factor for decentralization of solar power.

Chapter 10 looks into hydro-power decentralization. This chapter also looks at smart contracts, through an open-source project called hydro. Both of these technologies are viewed in light of decentralization of energy infrastructure. The chapter also shows how smart contracts may allow for individuals to take entrepreneurial steps into providing for themselves and the grid.

Chapter 11 explores the hesitancy of adopting renewable energy, and decentralization of energy production. This chapter explores why decentralization has been achieved with the technology available and the hesitancy of individuals, groups, corporations, and governments to decentralization. The overall consensus was that due to the stringent ecosystem of fossil fuels, and reliance on reliable power, decentralization has taken a back seat. Along side this, the reluctance to change and innovation from government actors and large corporations have stifled the innovation of energy decentralization.

www.ingramcontent.com/pod-product-compliance
Lightning Source LLC
Chambersburg PA
CBHW070233180526
45158CB00001BA/469